"Of all obstacles to a thoroughly penetrating account of existence, none looms up more dismayingly than 'time'. Explain time? Not without explaining existence. Explain existence? Not without explaining time..."[1]

John Archibald Wheeler

For time for to seek, And by truth to abide. To steadfastly speak, And in verse to confide...

The Infinite Tree

&

The Rivers of Time

Time, Experience, & The Foundations of Reality

Marc Garner

While this is a book about time and the emergent worlds of the quantum multiverse, the author is not a physicist, and makes no claim to the contrary. Throughout the book, notably in (but by no means restricted to) chapters 5, 10, 12, 17, 18 and 19, the author expresses his own opinions on a range of topics. These should neither be confused with, nor mistaken for, the views of any other person or persons referenced in the text.

First edition paperback in black and white, August 2021

*All artwork, photography, illustrations, and poetry by Marc Garner
unless otherwise stated.*

Cover design by Marc Garner, composited (with thanks) of imagery by NASA, ESA, Digitized Sky Survey 2 (Acknowledgement: Davide De Martin), Chris Schur, EpicStockMedia, Senee Sriyota, Shutterstock.com, and Marc Garner.

Back cover 'ouroboros' - Marc Garner, Vinap, Shutterstock.com

ISBN 978-1-9196294-0-7 (hardback in colour)
ISBN 978-1-9196294-1-4 (paperback in colour)
ISBN 978-1-9196294-4-5 (hardback in black and white)
ISBN 978-1-9196294-2-1 (paperback in black and white)
ISBN 978-1-9196294-3-8 (ebook)

Published by Shadowlands Media
www.shadowlandsmedia.co.uk

For Jessica, Freya, and Alexander,

With love drawn from a well as deep as time.

Contents

Part III - Quantum Spacetime

Part IV - The Rivers of Time

Part V - The Magnificence

Preface

What *is* time?

It's a question that I first puzzled over as a young boy. I remember the occasion well - The sunlight poured in through the windscreen of the car, illuminating the interior with a glowing soft light as it bathed us in the warmth of its rays. My father was at the wheel; my mother in the passenger seat; and my brother on the back seat beside me. Out of the window, the world flew by in a blur of green fields and fence-posts, beneath the comforting blanket of a warm and hazy summer sky.

We were in motion, dynamic and fluid, and so was the world. Seconds ticked by, and as they passed, they brought with them change. There was of course nothing out of the ordinary about the situation, but it was the first time that it had occurred to me to marvel at how it might happen. How exactly does that change come to be?

It might seem like a strange question to ask - everyone else certainly seemed to think so - but it is one that is fundamental to the world.

Through the glare of the sun, my eyes strained to capture the motion of the hands on my wristwatch, as I squinted to focus on the dial.

Tick. Tock. Tick. Tock.

The radio crackled and fizzed to the sounds of the sports report, and in the front of the car someone was talking, but I remained transfixed upon the motion of the hands.

Tick. Tock. Tick. Tock.

Time seems to carry us forwards relentlessly along its never-ebbing flow, but what really were these seconds that were ticking by? What was it that the hands were really counting off?

I was held mesmerized by its mystery, and it's a moment that stayed with me.

From the seeds that were planted that day, grew a life-long fascination with what I believe to be one of the deepest of questions that can be asked - what exactly, is this thing we call 'time'?

St. Augustine once mused that he felt he knew, so long as nobody asked him to explain it. For him, like most of us, I suspect the concept was one of his intuitive understanding. It is the idea that the world exists in a present moment; that the past is how it used to be, and that the future is how it might be going forwards.

It is the notion that we (along with everything else) are carried upon the crest of that ever-changing present moment, located at the very bleeding-edge of history as we are swept inextricably along towards the future. It is the idea that time can be represented as a neat line stretching away towards the right-hand side of a piece of paper; that one moment flows into the next; and that we live in a dynamically changing world. It is the belief that events happen at distinct and objectively identifiable moments, against the backdrop of a time that ticks away universally the same for all things in all places. It is the idea that it makes sense to speak of the time at which something happened; that the future is open; and that once it is gone, the past exists only as a memory.

It is this view that was assumed by Sir Isaac Newton when he wrote down his famed laws of motion in the 1600's, and it is the same view that is so deeply engrained into our psyche, that it is almost impossible to conceive of it being any other way. It is also, entirely wrong.

In 1905, Einstein published his astonishing theory of Special Relativity, and our conception of the nature of reality was transformed. Like a veil had been lifted from our eyes, no longer could we presume to trust that our everyday experience was representative of the true nature of the world, for in its glorious wonder, inescapably, that world is not what it seems...

Einstein's incredible discoveries began a revolution in our understanding that is still unfolding to this day. It is the purpose of this book to attempt to explore the remarkable insights of that revolution; to uncover the true nature of time; the character of the reality it implies; and to venture a tentative answer to the deep mystery of how a world so shockingly at odds with the one we perceive, can possibly give rise to the everyday experience of what it is to be human.

It is a journey through the extraordinary implications that flow as a consequence of Relativity, and the deep questions they pose to us with regards to the very foundations of reality. It will explore the challenges they present to our most basic of assumptions about human experience - assumptions about the nature of life and death, consciousness, identity, and free-will - and will reveal the basic dynamism of the world to be but an illusion.

There is, as we shall see, in fact no such thing as the flow of time. How this incredible truth can possibly be reconciled with the reality we suppose to experience, is the central mystery with which we shall be concerned.

The search for answers will lead us through some of the most incredible and profound discoveries of man, as we probe the revelations that lie at the very heart of existence through the remarkable lens of quantum physics, and discover how the universe, and the life that we know, might arise from it.

Sat in the car that day as a child, I had no way of knowing that right there with me were all of the elements of that mystery, which together, would one day form the answers I was seeking - the light; the motion; the space through which we moved; the intricate interplay of trillions of subatomic particles; the miraculous manner through which they relate; conscious experience; observation; and perhaps most astonishing of all - the thunderous silence of the splitting of worlds.

It is only now, after all these years, that I understand that the beauty of that day remains etched not only into my memory, but into the very fabric of reality itself. I'd like to share with you why.

This is the story of time...

Acknowledgements

There are many dualities that exist in the world, in life, and in ourselves. Some of them reside purely at the abstract level of language, concepts, and ideas, while others seem to reflect something deeper and more fundamental.

Human beings, for example, are at once capable of great kindness and generosity, yet great cruelty and spite; The cat is both predator to the bird, and prey to the Coyote; and death for the caterpillar is birth for the butterfly. These are dualities at the abstract level. They are born of the way we conceptualise and categorise things, and by the manner in which we make use of language.

At the more fundamental level, light is both a particle and a wave; an electron is both here and there (and both and neither); and there are dual descriptions of any region of space - one from the perspective of its bulk, and one from the perspective of its boundary. These are physical dualisms which sit somewhere close to base level of reality. They are not abstract ideas, but fundamental truths.

There is a similar sort of fundamental dualism which lies at the heart of time - a physical contradiction that defines our reality itself, and yet it was a dualism of the abstract kind which first inspired me to write about it. The twilight is at once the end of the day and the start of the night - a beautiful transition between states which, for me, captures the very essence of time. It holds an intrinsic splendour which encapsulates the beauty I find inherent to the world, and in thinking deeply about time, it is this image of perfect stillness merged with seamless transition to which my mind's eye always returns.

The world is a truly remarkable place, full of wonder and elegance, and the rules which govern it are stranger than we can suppose. In attempting to convey a sense of their majesty, I need to first acknowledge the towering intellects of the many giants upon whose shoulders I brazenly stand - men and women who represent the very pinnacle of scientific thought, and of whose jaw-dropping accomplishments I can only lyricise. I have tried to represent their genius faithfully in these pages, and any deficiencies in the text are mine, not theirs.

Secondly, I should like to express my thanks to my family for their enduring patience with my obsession, which has claimed more time than I would care to account for.

Finally, I'd like to thank all of those who have very generously given their own time to work through the many versions and drafts to provide feedback - feedback without which it would be an immeasurably poorer work.

In particular, I would like to thank Adam Cameron, Phil Pearce, Peter Walsh, and most of all, Chris Garner - my father, whom I think has probably seen and critiqued almost every draft since I began, and without whose endless support the words 'Bell Inequality' would likely have seen me reaching for the whisky bottle (more often).

Rising,

Arising,

The shape of the world,

From shadows emerging,

A tangible realm,

In that which is static,

Dynamics shall flow,

And time in the timeless,

The conscious will know...

I - The Everywhen.

"At last it came to me that time was suspect.."[2]

Albert Einstein

The Relativity of Time

The quest for knowledge is the unquenchable thirst of the human soul. Since the dawn of our species, it has driven us to push the boundaries of our understanding in the relentless pursuit of a deeper wisdom. It is the desire to know the world in which we live; to glimpse the wiring under the board; and ultimately to know ourselves, that we might better understand our place in the cosmos, who we are, and what (if anything) that might mean.

In the formative days of scientific thought, it is doubtful that anyone could have conceived of the understandings to which that thirst for knowledge would take us, or that even in their wildest speculations, anyone would have thought that in the study of how things move, were to be found such hidden secrets so profound.

Time, is our everything. The rhythmic beating heart of existence, to whose unerring silent pulse all things must dance. It is entwined so tightly with our experience, so as to go almost unconsidered - an unquestionable given that is so fundamental to the world, that we view it almost entirely without reproach.

While scholars and philosophers grapple with the workings of that world, it is time that is assumed as the ever-present background against which our toils are set. Things grow, shrink, live and die over time. The oceans swell; the seasons turn; day gives way to night, and night then turns to day. A projectile rises and falls on its trajectory as it arcs through the air, over time. Particles are born, collide, and decay, over time. And in the heavens, the stars burn brightly, before exhausting their fuel and eventually fading, over time.

We make the assumption there is a universal 'now' which is happening at all places, and that as an event occurs in say, London, there are events in other locations we can point to as happening 'at the same time'. The way in which we structure our thinking about the world is utterly dependent upon it. It is the universal clock that ticks away reliably in the background, providing a point of reference against which all things can be measured, regardless of their location in space, and independent of any perspective from which they are viewed.

Properly known as 'absolute time', it is essentially the idea that time exists independently of the universe and anything it contains. It is a concept so deeply embedded into the way that we think, that it's almost impossible to imagine it being anything but correct.

But what if I were to tell you that although the concept is innately intuitive to us, it also entirely wrong? What if I were to say that time in reality, bears little resemblance to the notion of it that we carry around with us in our minds? Perhaps you'd be intrigued, or perhaps not. But what if I went on to say that just as surely as you will one day reach the end of your days, you will also (and just as surely) live eternal? You'd perhaps suspect that I've lost my mind, and yet truth can be stranger than fiction, and as we shall see, reality more fantastical than we might reasonably suppose...

Our story begins in 1887, with the unexpected result obtained from an experiment carried out by A Michelson and E Morley. It had been the prevailing view at the time, that space must be filled by a mysterious substance called 'the luminiferous aether' (or 'the aether', for short), so-named after the Greek god of light. This belief was based upon the reasoning that as sound waves require a medium through which to travel, then the same must also be true of waves of light - an entirely reasonable assumption, given what was known at that point. Their experiment was intended to confirm the existence of this 'luminiferous aether'.

As an important item of note, this belief in the aether was set against a background in which scientific opinion was dominated by a 'Newtonian' world-view. That is to say, one that was very much inherited from Sir Isaac Newton - the great father of modern physics. It was way back in the 1600's that he penned his hugely successful laws of motion - laws which had sculpted and defined the entire system of scientific thought ever since, and which had stood unchallenged for more than two centuries. Those same laws are still taught in high-school classrooms to this day, and describe how objects move through the three dimensions of space, as forces act upon them over time. Time (and more specifically, the assumption that it is a reliable and universal clockwork-like background against which the world plays-out), is a central tenet of those laws.

Back with the aether, Michelson and Morley had designed their experiment to detect its presence by measuring the differences in the speed of light passing through it in different directions. It had been assumed that, due to an 'aether wind' caused by the motion of Earth through space, the speed of light would vary depending upon the direction in which it was travelling (due to it meeting resistance from the aether wind). Their shock at the actual outcome of their experiment must have been palpable, for it did not provide the unequivocal proof of the aether's existence for which they had been hoping. On the contrary - it instead demonstrated a constant speed of light, which in turn cast the existence of the aether into serious doubt.

New theories sprang up in an attempt to explain the result, and laid many of the mathematical foundations for what was to come, but it wasn't until the early years of the 20th century that the true revolution in our understanding began, when one Albert Einstein had the revelation of relativity. With it, and at a stroke, he not only explained away the experimental result of Michelson and Morley, but did away with the aether altogether. Both of these achievements paled into insignificance however, next to the fact that in doing so, he supplanted Newton's laws of motion with new laws of his own. These new laws encompassed Newton's original ones, but showed them to be a rough approximation to a deeper truth - an approximation appropriate only in the restricted context of objects moving at everyday speeds. When concerned with objects moving with much greater velocity (or when a higher degree of precision is demanded), Einstein's deeper, and more generally applicable laws are required. He showed the equations of Newton to be a 'zoomed-out' blurring of a much more subtle reality - a reality which by any stretch of the imagination, and in anyone's terms, is remarkable.

Einstein's theory became known as 'Special Relativity', and central to the whole idea, was the conjecture that the speed of light is naturally constant in a vacuum, regardless of any inertial frame of reference. That is to say, that light **always** moves at the same speed through space, no matter the perspective from which it is viewed (hence the constant speed of light observed in the Michelson-Morley experiment). While a seemingly innocuous prediction at first-glance, its earth-shattering consequences would prove to be astonishing, for not only would they tear down the very foundations of the Newtonian scientific orthodoxy, but would lay waste to our common-sense and intuitive view of time, in its entirety.

To see why, consider the classic example of a simple light clock constructed of two mirrors, as shown in figure 1.1. The clock operates by constantly bouncing a photon (a 'particle' of light) back and forth between the mirrors.

Figure 1.1

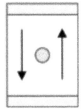

The time it takes the photon to travel from one mirror to the other can be thought of as a 'tick' of the clock. Alternatively, we could take the time it takes for the photon's round-trip (bouncing from one mirror to the other and back again) to represent one tick. The choice is arbitrary and makes no difference for our purposes.

Irrespective of whatever we take to represent a tick, Einstein said that the speed of the light travelling between the mirrors must remain constant (299,792,458 metres per second), regardless of the perspective from which it is viewed. This seems completely natural for the case where both the clock and anyone observing it are all at rest (I.e. not moving relative to each other) - all stationary observers agree that the photon travels a distance 'd' between the mirrors. They all see it moving at the same speed, and everything is as we might naturally expect it to be.

Figure 1.2

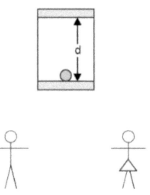

Let's tale a look at what would happen however, if the clock were not stationary, but was instead moving past one of the observers at high speed while the other travelled with it. Let's imagine that it's being carried aboard a rocket piloted by one of the observers, Alice, while her friend Bob remains on the ground.

So far as Alice (moving with the clock aboard the rocket) is concerned, she is still stationary with respect to the clock. That is, they are moving *with* each other as opposed to *relative* to each other, and as such share the same inertial frame of reference. For this reason, the relationship between her and the clock remains the same as it did in the stationary example - Alice still sees the photon as travelling the distance d between the two mirrors.

Figure 1.3

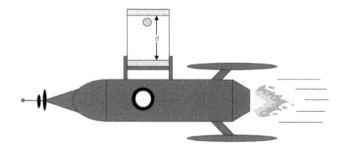

Bob however, sees a different situation. As the rocket is moving past him, then so too are the mirrors of the clock. This puts him and the clock in different frames of reference. To Bob, the photon is traversing a greater distance than it would if the clock were stationary, because it is tracing a diagonal between the moving mirrors

Figure 1.4

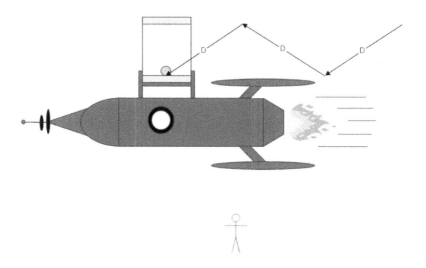

So here we have a paradox - from the perspective of Alice, with each tick the photon travels a distance d, but from the perspective of Bob, with each tick it travels a greater distance D. But it is the one and the same photon they are both looking at!

So if, as according to Einstein, the speed of the photon is the same from both perspectives, yet the distance it must travel between the mirrors is different, then the time it must take to cover that distance must also be different. Or put another way, the amount of time it takes for a particular set of events to occur from Bob's perspective, is different from the amount of time it takes the same set of events to occur from Alice's.

And this is in fact, exactly what happens - Bob bears witness to the photon taking longer to bounce between the mirrors than Alice does.

So which perspective is correct? - his or hers? And here is the genius of Einstein's great realisation - they both are. There is no one perspective that is any more valid than another, and the competing viewpoints of Bob and Alice are both correct within their respective frames of reference.

There is no over-arching 'master' or 'universal' view that can be considered as containing the ultimate or absolute truth, because there **is** no absolute truth. It is literally a question of relative perspective.

They both look at the same photon, and yet Bob sees it taking a longer time to bounce between the mirrors than Alice does, and they are both right.

We must be careful with the wording we use here. Perhaps due to the incredible implications, we can often read about examples such as the one given above, and find them couched in language which softens or dilutes their meaning. We might find the use of phrases such as 'To Bob, it *appears* as though time is running slowly on the rocket', but this is to profoundly miss the point. I've italicised the word 'appears' because it is misleading. Time does not *appear* to be running at different rates for he and Alice - time **is** running at different rates for them, and it is due to their relative motion.

In order to preserve a constant speed of light from all points of view, time actually warps and dilates with respect to the observer.

Neither Bob nor Alice *feel* as though the rate at which time passes has changed for themselves - they both feel as though it has changed for the other. Each inertial frame of reference behaves as though it is stationary - as though it's the rest of the world that is moving. So from within each frame it looks as though it's the other that has changed.

In spite of the momentous gravity of its repercussions, Einstein's theory was well understood and roundly accepted. The math was rigorous and indisputable, and its predictions exquisitely accurate. The idea of the aether was hence thereafter consigned to history, and along with it, our overly simplistic and naïve conception of time. Newtons laws of motion - some of the main bastions of physical science up until that point - were relegated to a secondary status, useful only where low velocities were concerned or where approximate results would suffice, and the crowning glory of the greatest scientist in history was supplanted by the work of a mere patents clerk - Einstein. (Albeit one that would turn out to be in possession of one of the finest intellects the human race has ever produced).

It is difficult to overstate the size and significance of this seismic shift in understanding, but any lingering vestiges of doubt that may have remained were later categorically put to rest through a remarkable series of ingenious experiments, all of which confirmed Einstein's theory. The first of these was performed by H. E. Ives and G. R. Stilwell in 1938, entitled *"An experimental study of the rate of a moving atomic clock"*, and was repeated to a higher degree of accuracy by those same experimentalists in 1941. Meanwhile, a similar test was carried out to equal success by Bruno Rossi and D. B. Hall in 1940, though by different means - the Ives-Stilwell experiments made use of the relative frequencies of light arriving from a source that was in motion with respect to a 'stationary' observer, whereas the Rossi-Hall one derived its results from the relativistic decay of high-speed particles in the atmosphere.

Further experiments continued throughout the 20th century, with Frisch and Smith in 1963, and perhaps most famously by Joseph Hafele and Richard Keating in 1971, who took a group of synchronised atomic clocks, and flew some of them around the world on commercial airliners while leaving the others behind at the United States Naval Observatory. The idea was that because they had been moving relative to one another, once brought back together and compared, the clocks that had travelled aboard the airliners would be found to be no longer in-sync with those which had remained at rest on the ground. In fact, they would be found to be running slow by comparison, having been subject to the time dilation which relativity predicts. The experiment, as with all others before it, was a resounding success - not only were the clocks that had been in motion found to be behind the ones that had not, they were also slow by the amount Special Relativity predicted.

These days, time-dilation is routinely confirmed by undergraduate experiments, and is sometimes even demonstrated as a kind of nerdy party trick, as was (arguably) the case in a 1996 re-enactment of the Hafele-Keating experiment to mark the 25th anniversary of its original performance. In fact, so far has the experimental envelope been pushed, that time dilation has even been confirmed at everyday speeds as low as 36 km/h - that's the sort of speed that a top athlete is able to sprint at (at the time of writing, the present-day sprint record stands at the incredible 44.72 km/h attained by Usain Bolt in 2009)...

The inescapable conclusion is that there is simply no way of speaking about how much time has passed in any sort of generalised and universal sense, for it has passed in different measure for each thing, depending upon the motion it has had. Events in space cannot be thought of as happening at absolute times - they instead have times that are relative to each other, and how much time we experience as having passed is governed by our individual perspectives. As everything in the universe is in motion with respect to something else (nothing is truly at rest - something 'at rest' on Earth still has motion relative to the Sun, which in turn has motion relative to other celestial objects, etc), then each perspective is just as valid as the next.

The reason we are able to construct for ourselves the illusion of a single unified passage of time, is that the rates at which it is typically passing for us and the things we encounter, tend to be very similar - and that is due to their tendency of being in close-by places, and moving at relatively low speeds in comparison to the speed of light. The spectacularly miniscule amounts by which time dilation occurs for objects moving at everyday speeds, leads us to the mistaken perception that time is passing at a consistent rate for all things. But it is not. The differences are just so small as to be typically imperceptible to us. But make no mistake, they are there.

If we (or the objects to which we compare our motion) were to move at speeds approaching the speed of light, then those differences would become much more pronounced, and would certainly be noticed. Let's take a look at what would happen, for example, if Alice were to fly her rocket away to Alpha Centauri (the nearest star system) and back again at 99.9% of the speed of light.

At such high velocity compared to that of Bob (waiting dutifully behind on Earth), time for Alice, the rocket, and everything aboard would run quite significantly slower than it would for he. All processes aboard the rocket - be they physical, chemical, biological, or otherwise - would be subject to this relative slowing of time. There is nothing that is immune or impervious to it - it is all-pervading, and totally encompassing of everything within the inertial frame of the rocket.

By way of comparison to Bob, the biological aging of Alice would be slowed by every bit as much as the ticking of her clock. In this particular example, once we account for the turn-around and reversal of her direction of motion at the half-way point of her journey, then upon their reunion back on Earth, they would find him to have aged by about eight years in contrast to a miserly four months (approx.) for she.

The world in which we live - this cathedral so mighty - is a strange and extraordinary place, where time is not something which is global, but is rather a phenomenon that is local to each object. It warps, it dilates, and it bends to the light. What Einstein showed, is that in order to have a hope of understanding that world, we must abandon our common-sense notion of time, completely. It is just as well that we do, for the discovery of its relative dilation was just the beginning...

Things were about to get much, much stranger...

Your today,

- My tomorrow's Sun rising,

Our moments replete,

In their fullness and truth,

With velocity soaring,

I survey your approach,

In thrall to your motion,

Time ages you slow.

The now,

The then,

The Everywhen,

The jewel of creation,

Revealed to mere men...

Spacetime

&

The Simultaneity of Events

Contrary to popular belief, it was not Einstein, but his former professor - the eminent mathematician Hermann Minkowski - who first had the realisation that his former student's theory of Special Relativity is properly understood in terms of a 4-dimensional geometry. Minkowski combined the previously independent concepts of space and time into a single continuum, which we call 'Spacetime'.

Einstein had demonstrated that time runs at different rates for different observers, and that no one perspective is any more valid than another, but it was Minkowski who went on to correctly deduce the full physical implications of the new theory.

In 1908, he gave an address called 'Space and Time', to the 80th Assembly of German Natural Scientists and Physicians, which opened with the now famous line:

"The views of space and time which I wish to lay before you have sprung from the soil of experimental physics, and therein lies their strength. They are radical. Henceforth space by itself, and time by itself, are doomed to fade away into mere shadows, and only a kind of union of the two will preserve an independent reality."

He went on to describe a fabric of reality which is not the 3-dimensional world that we might suppose, but which is instead a strange kind of landscape comprised of three space-like dimensions, and a 4th which is time-like. Those dimensions of space and time are inextricably connected as different aspects of the same remarkable object - an extraordinary thing called 'Spacetime'.

It is an alien concept which can, upon first encounter, be difficult to wrap your head around. Einstein himself initially struggled to accept it, though his eventual adoption of it allowed him to ultimately go on to create his crowning glory in 1915 - his General Theory of Relativity. That theory elaborates upon this idea of Spacetime as a geometry, and introduces the idea that time is not only deformed by the motions of objects, but by gravitating masses too. At the time of Minkowski's address though, this was not known. It makes little difference to our interest here however, which are the primary ramifications of a 4-dimensional world...

Minkowski correctly conceived of reality as a single block containing everything from the beginning of time, through to its very end. Due to its inherent nature, this is sometimes referred to as the 'Block Universe'. It is represented here in figure 1.5, where for the purpose of visualisation, it is illustrated as two dimensions of space, and one of time.

Figure 1.5

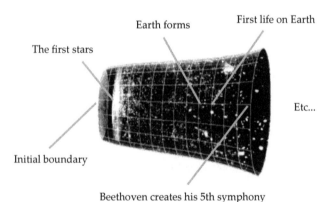

The first stars

Earth forms

First life on Earth

Etc...

Initial boundary

Beethoven creates his 5th symphony

In spite of the obvious limitations of the illustration, hopefully the concept is relatively clear - the full 3-dimensional contents of space co-exist with each other simultaneously at different points in time, and together, they form a kind of landscape which exists as a single block of reality called 'Spacetime'.

It is the entire universe, across the full breadth of time.

To understand why he was right about this being a reflection of the true nature of the world, let us return to the example of Alice piloting the rocket. Let's suppose she is travelling at half the speed of light as she approaches Bob, who is 'stationary'. As we have already discovered, because of her great velocity compared to his, time is not passing at an equal rate for them. Let's say that from Bob's point of view, five seconds before Alice passes him, he activates a flashlight he has pointed in her direction. From Alice's perspective, she sees this happen 2.8868 seconds before their paths cross (because she is moving towards the light, which is also moving towards her). Once we've adjusted for how long it takes the light from the torch to reach her, we can deduce that in her frame of reference, Bob switched on the torch 5.7735 seconds before their paths crossed.

So Bob and Alice have differing versions of history, with Alice experiencing a version whereby Bob turned on the torch 0.7735 seconds earlier than he did in his version. If they were to later meet and compare notes, they would realise that she had encountered him activating the light before he had done it…

How can this be? How can one person encounter another carrying out an act that they haven't even yet done from their own point of view? It's a deep and important question, because if time is passing at different rates for different objects, then this must literally be happening all the time.

The simple and shockingly profound answer, is that it's because the future is already there... and it is this which leads to the picture of Minkowski's Spacetime block.

The actions that we are going to take, and the events we are going to witness, are all pe-determined and pre-existing within the Spacetime block. What's more, those events are every bit as physically real as the events that we consider to be happening 'right now'.

The past, present, and future all exist on an equal footing. Or more accurately, to objectively split time into those three concepts is inherently false. There is only any validity to them from the subjective point of view of something (or someone) at a given Spacetime location. They are relative concepts in an absolute whole which draws no overall distinction between past, present, and future.

The landscape of Spacetime contains within it everything that is, everything that ever was, and everything that will ever come to be. It is in its completeness, all things at all times. It is the Everywhen.

Events that we think of as being in the past, are only actually in the past from whatever our current perspective happens to be. Similarly, future events are only in the future compared to our Spacetime location. If they are in our future, then all that means is that we happen to have not 'reached' them yet.

Building upon this great insight, Minkowski realised that the Spacetime block may be thought of as being 'sliced-up' into instants of time, each containing the full 3-dimensional contents of space at that given instant.

Figure 1.6

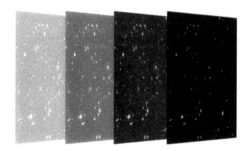

Marc Garner / Egyptian Studio / Shutterstock.com

These slices are planes along which events can be thought of as happening 'at the same time' **from the perspective of a particular observer**. They are sometimes referred to as 'planes of simultaneity', in the sense that events located along them have the appearance of happening simultaneously for a particular observer. They are essentially discreetly defined moments of time as viewed from a particular perspective. From this point onwards, we will refer to them as 'Now Slices'.

They can be thought of in much the same way as the individual frames of a movie. They are frozen snapshots of the universe, and stacked together in the correct order, they form a sequence of events that unfolds therein.

Minkowski realised that what constitutes a Now Slice depends upon the viewpoint of the observer, and that the angle at which it cuts through the universe is dictated by their motion. Changing how you are moving, not only alters the rate at which time passes for you, but also what is happening 'now' from your point of view.

To see why this is, consider the differing perspectives of Alice and Bob in the following examples. In order to preserve our sanity, I'm plotting just one space-like dimension, along with the time-like dimension. Let's start with the viewpoint of Bob, who for the sake of simplicity, we shall take to be stationary.

Figure 1.7

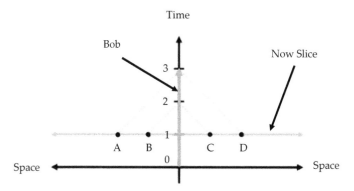

The diagram in figure 1.7 is scaled such that light rays cut through it at an angle of 45⁰. These are represented by the dotted lines. As Bob is not moving through space (I.e. is moving only through time), he traces a history (shown by the grey arrow) that moves vertically up the time axis. At t=2, he becomes aware of events B and C, as light emitted from them intersects with his position. A second later at t=3, he becomes aware of events A and D. Because of the distance the light has travelled from his perspective, he infers that all events A, B, C, and D happened at the same time (t=1).

For Bob, Now Slices run horizontally across our diagram, in lines which are parallel with the space axis.

Now let's add Alice into the situation, and again have her travelling at half the speed of light (and on this occasion, away from Bob through space).

Figure 1.8

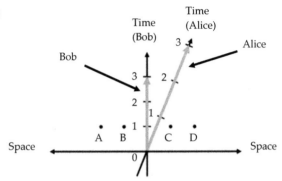

From Bob's perspective, the history she traces through the environment (Spacetime) runs away to his right as she moves away from him through space. As time is something which is personalised for each observer, her time axis is angled with her, and because of her great velocity, the ticks of her clock are stretched by comparison with his (note the wider gap between the intervals on her time axis). But these are not the only differences, and figure 1.8 is not yet a strictly accurate representation of the true situation.

As we have already learned, space and time are not *really* independent of each other. Because of this, where Alice's time axis becomes skewed by a certain angle, then the same fate must too befall her space axis, and to the same degree.

Yes, you did read that right - just as their relative experience of time becomes distorted by motion, so too does their experience of space.

Figure 1.9 is a more accurate illustration than figure 1.8, because it has both time **and** space tilted at an incline for Alice relative to Bob.

Figure 1.9

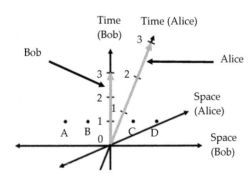

I personally find this relative bending of space even more mind-boggling than the warping of time. It is, in my opinion, one of the most difficult concepts in all of physics, but let's put questions of space gently to one side for now, and focus instead upon what happens with regards to time.

Her time axis may be angled by comparison to Bob's, but the light rays move through the environment independently of this (in fact, independently of the angle of *anyone's* space or time axes). As such, and because of the different scales and angles of the two sets of space and time axes, they intersect with our friends differently.

Figure 1.10

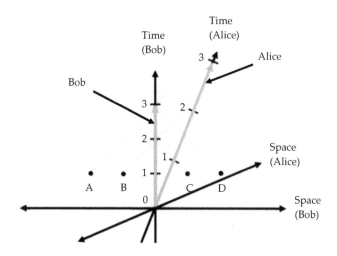

From figure 1.10, we can see that the light from event D, for example, reaches Bob at t=3, but reaches Alice somewhere between t=1 and t=2. Similarly, light from event B reaches Bob at t=2, but somewhere between t=2 and t=3 for Alice.

When they each work backwards to account for how far the light has travelled, they come to different conclusions as to which events are happening 'at the same time'.

Bob, for instance, maintains that A, B, C, and D all occur together, as we have seen previously.

Figure 1.11

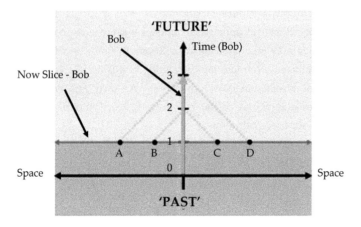

Alice however, curious though it may be, experiences a history with a different order of events. Or put another way - her Now Slices cut through Spacetime at a different angle.

Figure 1.12

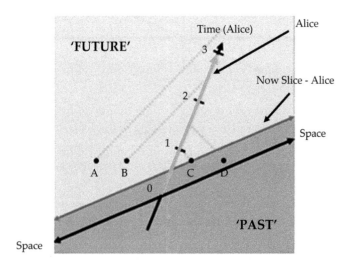

They still run in parallel to the space axis, but importantly, it is **her** space axis they are parallel to - not his. So far as Alice is concerned, event D happened before event C, and events A and B come later. So they disagree upon the contents of their moments of time. From the previous chapter, we know that there is no given perspective which is any more (or any less) valid than the next, and we are forced to conclude that there is no objective truth as to which sets of events are happening at any given time. It is literally a matter of perspective.

Let's take a little time (if you'll excuse the pun) to examine the consequences of this a little closer. Let's imagine our two friends are this time located a great distance apart, in different regions of Spacetime. If they are at rest with respect to one another, then they might share the same view as to which events are happening 'now'. I.e. They might both agree upon a common Now Slice:

Figure 1.13

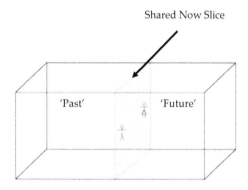

Shared Now Slice

'Past'   'Future'

Let's say that Alice then sets off in motion, in a direction that carries her away from Bob. This changes the angle of her Now Slice. The greater the velocity of her motion, the larger the angle, and the direction in which she moves determines whether that angle is oriented towards Bob's past or towards his future. In this case, as she is moving away from him, she is angled towards his past.

Figure 1.14

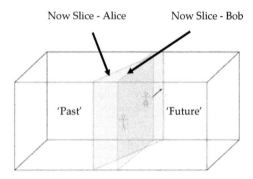

For Alice, many of the things that are happening 'now' are events that Bob considers to be in the past. They include the things that he has already done from his own perspective, and indeed, the version of Bob that Alice considers 'currently' living, is a version that the Bob in our illustration regards as a mere memory.

If she then turns around and moves in the opposite direction, then the angle of her Now Slice is reversed. What she now considers to be the present, is largely in the future according to Bob (including actions that our Bob himself is yet to carry out).

Figure 1.15

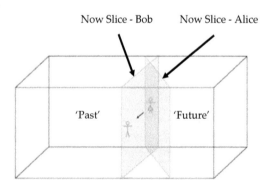

In this way, provided she is travelling quickly enough, she is able to encounter a 'future' version of Bob, and see him turning on the torch before he has done it from the perspective of his own Now Slice.

Objects in Spacetime are simultaneously present at all their time-like locations. This is why Alice is able to see a future version of Bob - because all versions of Bob that ever exist can be found somewhere within the landscape. So to describe an object (such as Bob, for example) in its totality, you have to describe it across all of its temporal locations. We call this the 'world-line' of an object, and have encountered the concept already in figures 1.7 to 1.12 without calling it out as such. There, I refer to their world-lines as the histories which they trace through Spacetime. Another common way of speaking about world-lines is to call them 'paths', and I will use all of these terms interchangeably throughout the course of the book.

Having established the picture of the 4-dimensional Spacetime block, we can explore this idea of world-lines a little further, and see that the world-line of an object that moves in a circle through space, would look like a coil in Spacetime:

Figure 1.16

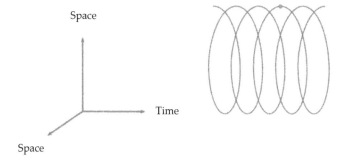

This represents the object over the full course of its existence. The grey dot shows it as it appears at one particular instant of time - at one Now Slice. It is from the perspective of such instants that we are used to seeing things, but as all of time exists all at once, then when correctly viewed as an objective whole, the object in question is not really a dot at all, but a coil, and has no real motion. Objectively, it is something which is entirely static.

Everything in Spacetime is this way - our 'coil' illustrated here, Bob, Alice, you, me, the Earth, Moon, Sun, and stars... none of them really have any motion. There is in fact no *real* motion at all in Spacetime. If an observer were somehow able to look in from the outside, they would find an entirely static world, where nothing ever changes. It is only from the subjective view of someone experiencing time moment-by-moment, that the illusion of a dynamically changing world is created.

Spacetime itself, and everything it contains, is forever frozen. Nothing has ever moved, and nothing ever will. There is no 'present moment' sweeping forth through the Spacetime block. There is in fact, simply no such thing as the passage of time at all - there is just... time. All of it, and all at once.

This remarkable truth of course jars dramatically with our everyday experience - we do not experience all of time all at once, and we certainly do not experience it as something which is static. On the contrary, we perceive ourselves as living in a dynamic and ever-changing present, rushing forwards *through* time as we march inescapably onwards to the future. How can the certainty with which we live this experience, be squared with the reality that we know it to contradict?

It is this juxtaposition that is the central mystery with which this book is concerned. **When the river of time is so definitively frozen, why do we so surely suppose it to flow?** In fact, why do we experience time at all?

We have covered some quite technical concepts in these early chapters, and the reader should not feel too alarmed if they have not quite internalised every precise detail. If there are in fact only a couple of points that you take away from the entire first part of the book, they should be that **all of time exists all at once**, and that **our world in reality, is something which is entirely static.** I wanted to cover the ideas that lead up to these truths in some detail, because it is they which form the basis of the questions for which we are going to seek answers. The block universe provides the scientific grounding for the issue that so perplexed me as a child - exactly what **is** the passage of time?

That search for answers will lead us eventually, to perhaps the most astonishing realisation of all.

Firstly though (and for the remainder of Part 1), we shall continue to explore the implications of a static and 4-dimensional reality, for there are further revelations that lie in wait, and they pose further questions equally profound...

Does the moon not wax and wane?
So shall the waves then roll not forth?

"There is no dynamics within Spacetime itself: nothing ever moves therein; nothing happens; nothing changes [...] one does not think of particles as 'moving through' Spacetime, or as 'following along' their world-lines. Rather, particles are just 'in' Spacetime, once and for all, and the world-line represents, all at once, the complete life history of the particle."[3]

R. Geroch

No life in death,

Is made undone,

But ever reigns,

From whence begun.

The Eternals

Many minds in which to ponder,
The many minds you've called your own...

In the previous chapter we have seen that time is woven into the very fabric of the world. It does not have an existence independent of space - rather time and space are simply different aspects of the same thing. They are inseparable attributes of a universe constructed of a union of them both - a union called 'Spacetime'.

From this it is clear that time is a purely internal property of the universe. It makes no sense to ask what existed before the universe began, for example, because when it comes to the universe as a whole, there is no such concept as 'before'. Time does not exist outside of it - it is something which is purely exclusive to the interior.

Figure 1.17

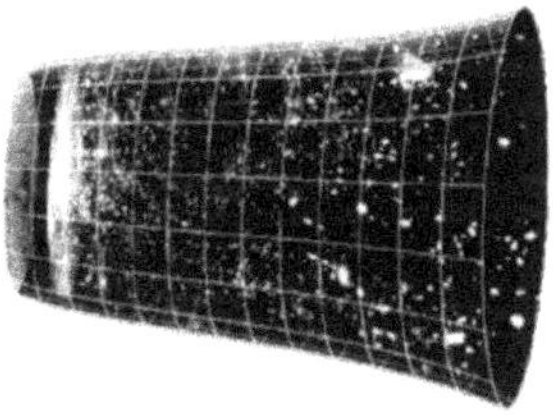

No time out here

ALL of time in there

No time out here

No time out here

Marc Garner / NASA

Following this through, we can see that the universe did not 'begin' in the strictest sense of the word. Its so-called beginning is simply a boundary condition at one end of an eternal object - at one end of Spacetime.

With time being an intrinsic part of the internal geometry, and with there being no external time against which that geometry can evolve, the universe is therefore exclusively static; unchanging; and fixed. It does not grow, and it does not age, for it is already all 'just there' across the entire fullness of time.

There are many issues - both philosophical and physical - which are raised by this. Perhaps the most stunning amongst them, is the inescapable conclusion that it renders the universe eternal. I single this out for particular attention, because if the universe is eternal then so too, by definition, are its contents.

Let's consider again what's happening when the angle of Alice's Now Slice is altered by her 'motion':

Figure 1.18

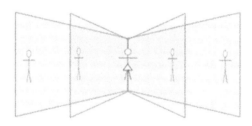

Wherever it is angled, so long as it cuts through the Spacetime block in places that are times within Bob's lifetime, she can find a version of him alive and well in that particular moment. This is extraordinary, for it means that there are versions of us (and everything else, of course) located at each and every instant in which we ever existed, and each and every instant that we ever will. We persist physically at all of the moments of our lives - Every fragment that makes up our world-lines is a living, breathing occurrence of ourselves.

Let's just pause for a second and properly digest what that means...

In the 1960's, my grandfather used to fish the local rivers of his hometown - a small Irish village called Cappamore. He is still there, fishing those rivers as we speak. Although he has already passed-on from the perspective of my current Now Slice, those moments in the 60's where he fished those waters are still objectively very real, and continue to exist in Spacetime in a very physical way - not just as a memory, or a record, but as a current reality that is every bit as valid as my own.

He will always be there, casting his rod (and if the truth be told, hurling dynamite into the water in a not-so-subtle attempt to cheat in the local fishing contest, but that's another story), just as he will always be continually living out every other moment of his remarkable life. He permanently exists at every Now Slice he was ever a part of - he always has, and he always will, and the same is true of each and every one of us.

We, along with everything else, are all eternal. There are versions of each of us at every moment that we ever existed, and at every moment we ever will, perpetually living out those moments forever.

This was a point made very poignantly by Einstein in a touching letter to the widow of his recently deceased friend, Besso -

"Now he has again preceded me a little in parting from this strange world. This has no importance. For people like us who believe in physics, the separation between past, present and future has only the importance of an admittedly tenacious illusion."[4]

Albert Einstein

Every moment remains forever a living monument - frozen; unchanging; real; physical; abiding; static; and eternal. Nothing ever really dies - its existence is just bounded to certain regions of the Spacetime block, and every occasion; event; happening; and experience remains forever as real, present, and current as it ever was.

Somewhere in Spacetime, I am 'right now' living out the moment of my first kiss. Somewhere else, I am watching with horror as the stone I've just thrown sails through the south window of the school sports hall. And there will always be somewhere that I am forever sat writing this sentence.

To learn that we are - in this sense - immortal, must rank as one of the most truly incredible discoveries of man. To die is to reach the end of your road, but that road remains in place regardless, and you never stop walking it. Death is just the point beyond which you have no existence at further Now slices.

As thrilling and astonishing as this is, the block universe has further surprises in store, and they are utterly confounding.

Consider, for instance, where the discussion leads if we pose the question of how many such eternal snapshot instances of ourselves exist through the course of our world-lines.

Max Planck demonstrated that the shortest possible unit length of space was approximately 1.6×10^{-35} metres. This is the smallest chunk that space can be carved up into, and is a quantity we call the 'Planck length'. The 'Planck time', is the corresponding natural unit of time. It is the time that it takes for individual packets of light (photons) to travel a distance of one Planck length in a vacuum. It is assumed to be the smallest theoretically measurable unit length of time, and there are 5.39×10^{44} of them in a second.

If we assume that you, the reader, live for about eighty years (please forgive me if I'm cutting your time too short!), then that would mean there are approximately 1,359,832,320,000,000,000,000,000,000,000,000,000,000, 000,000,000,000 living versions of you to be found in Spacetime (and this is assuming that you have only one history - we shall return to this issue later).

Just as you are conscious and aware right now, there's an almost identical copy of you, atom for atom, just a Planck time behind you. They are also conscious and aware - just as much as you are. Both of you probably have the idea that you are the one and only version of you, and you are both wrong. Neither one of you has any more right than the other to claim to be the canonical 'you'. The truth, in reality, is that there are about 325,987,200,000,000,000,000,000,000,000,000,000,000,000,000,000 versions of you from last week alone, all busy living out all the moments you think 'you' experienced in the last seven days.

There are of course, many versions of you located forwards in time from your 'current' location too. Some of them might be contemplating the time from their past when they first read this text, perhaps a little troubled by the notion that you are reading it right now, as they grapple with the question of whether or not you are they.

The fact is though, that each of our doppelgangers - be they from the 'past' or the 'future' - live concurrent with each other, and in light of this, there is a question of whether or not it's still valid that we think of ourselves as single entities existing across many points in time. Was our traditional view ever sound, or should we instead consider each temporally separated instance of ourselves to be a distinct entity in its own right?

This dilemma is illustrated in figure 1.19.

Figure 1.19

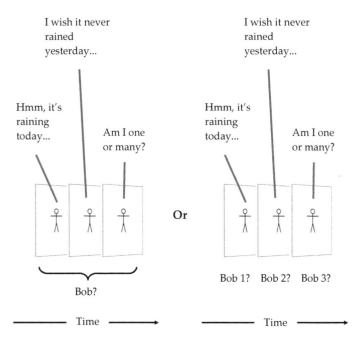

Most of us *feel* as though we are the former - that we are each single beings progressing through the moments of our lives. Yet we need to be careful, for as we have seen, things do not 'move along' their world lines at all, and time does not flow. Our *feeling* on this is sometimes said to have its roots in the fact that we view 'the past' differently to the way we view 'the future', which in turn is due to possessing memories which tell us about one, and only imaginings to tell us about the other.

Consider, for instance, the versions of Bob existing at the different Now Slices in figure 1.20.

Figure 1.20

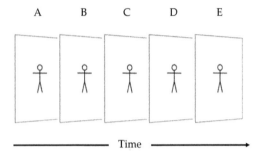

Let's take the example of the Bob who is at Now Slice C. As the moments shown are arranged in order of increasing time, then slice C is an evolution of slices A and B, and as such the Bob it contains has a brain which is configured with memories of what the world was like at those slices. Conversely, his brain is **not** configured with memories of what the world is like at slices D and E. Instead, it is probably filled with hopes (or perhaps fears) and expectations of what things *might* be like in those moments.

As a result, Bob C feels that he owns the experiences from slices A and B, but not those from slices D and E. This leads him to conclude that he has experienced moments A and B directly. In fact though, he only has an indirect experience of them (through the apparatus of his memory).

His viewpoint is re-enforced by physical manifestations other than memory, which lend weight to his claim that he was directly present at 'previous' moments. If, for example, he suffered a collision which left him with an injury at slice A, then that injury might still be present at slice C, and causing him pain. So he would have both the memory of the collision, and the physical evidence to back up the idea that it was him which it happened to.

So is he correct? Is he all of the previous Bobs? Or because they all live concurrent with each other, and are all aware, thinking, and experiencing (all individually, and all at once), are they in fact separate individuals deceived into a conviction of their singularity through an illusion created by memory?

Such a situation as the one in which we find ourselves in the Everywhen, where there are many sentient copies of ourselves, all forever living out single isolated moments of our lives, forces us to pause and re-evaluate exactly what it is that we think we mean, when we talk of the 'I' which we presume to be.

If the issue of time's flow is one of the great questions the reality of a block universe poses for us, then this is another. We shall return to it in the final stages of our investigation, where we hope to find a resolution to this most unsettling of puzzles.

In the meantime, if you are able to form an opinion one way or the other as to where you stand on this question of self in a 4-dimensional reality, I'd suggest you're probably doing rather well…

"I know who I was when I got up this morning, but I think I must have been changed several times since then."[5]

Lewis Carroll

(Alice's Adventures in Wonderland)

Come cry thee not for all the fallen,

Dry the tears upon your face,

Where lived they once they live forever,

In Spacetime's never-ending grace.

At intersections of our living,

A happy beauty lies,

Outside of which though distance parts us,

No-one really dies.

The Identity of a Moment

We naturally think of moments as being amenable to tagging with external labels, such as numbers representing 'dates' and 'times' which are universal.

Figure 1.21

| 11: 48: 31 | 11: 48: 32 | 11: 48: 33 |

This is an artefact of our delusion that there is some kind of external clock providing an absolute measure of time for all things. But as we have seen, reality doesn't work this way. The concept of 'now' is a relative one that is personalised for every observer, and precisely which events are happening at any given moment can (and do) vary from perspective to perspective.

The angle at which our personal Now Slices are oriented through the Everywhen, and indeed the rate at which time passes for each of us, is dictated by the subjective 'motion' that we each have individually.

We label different times and speak of them as though they are shared collectively, and it is of great practicality to do so, but it is just an approximation. We get away with it because of two things - the first is that we move at low speed, so the angles of our Now Slices differ only imperceptibly. The second is that we are located close to each other in space, so those miniscule differences in angles are not applied over great enough distances for us to see them amount to any significant differences in content (not over the distances with which we are concerned, anyway). So for most practical purposes, we can readily indulge in our fantasy.

We can make arrangements with friends or colleagues to meet at certain (imaginarily shared) times, and for the level of accuracy we require for that, it works just fine. We can schedule television listings, sporting events, and flights using the pretence of a universal time, as it's accurate enough for us to do so. We can arrange our lives around the concept of shared Nows, and it works because our actual Nows are similar enough that for the vast majority of the time, the minute differences between them are of no practical consequence.

But it **is** a delusion. When absolute precision is required over extended periods of time (in situations such as space flight, for example), then corrections for the relativistic effects of time dilation have to be taken into account, and corrected for. GPS satellites, for example, are only able to provide positioning information to the level of accuracy they do, because they make corrections for the fact that time is passing at a different rate for them than it is on the surface of the Earth. I.e. the differences between the content of their Now Slices and those of people on the surface, is enough to cause a problem were it not accounted for. (Actually, this difference is caused not only by their motion relative to the Earth, but as we shall see in a subsequent chapter, by the effects of Einstein's later theory of General Relativity too, but the point is that there is a time differential that needs to be corrected for).

So we can keep our approximations, and where they fail, we can make adjustments so that they remain useful, but if we want to speak about actual reality, then there are no external labels that it makes sense to apply to each moment. They are all subjective, so it is instead better to think of them as being defined by their content.

Like playing cards, or the pages of this book, true instants of time are distinguished by the information content that is 'printed on their faces'. The arrangement of matter and energy contained within the 3-dimensional space that each Now Slice embodies, may be thought of as forming a sort of unique 'timestamp' that identifies subjective moments as being distinct from one another.

Figure 1.22

Figure 1.22 shows three such moments in a universe of two particles. Each moment is defined by the configuration of the things it contains.

The 'distance' between such moments, can be thought of as the difference in the 3-dimensional information content they embody.

Examining that content closer, Relativity tells us that not only is there no universal clock ticking away merrily in the background, but that there is also no universal co-ordinate system that is somehow etched into the fabric of space. Objects in space do not have a position relative to the canvas of space itself - they only have position relative to each other.

If you imagine a world in which there existed only one particle, then that particle would have nothing with which it could have a position relative to, and as such, there would be nothing with respect to which its position could change.

In a world without change, there are no information deltas to distinguish different states - different moments; different Now Slices. If there are no differences in state to be distinguished, then there is no time. Time is the measure of change between states. It is nothing more.

Figure 1.23

With nothing to have a position relative to, the position of the only particle in a single-particle world cannot change.

Similarly, in a world with many particles that are subjectively stationary with respect to one another, then there is no change of state, and hence no difference in time.

Figure 1.24

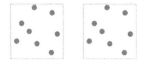

It is only as things change with respect to one another (due to the different shapes and angles they create in the static Spacetime block), that distinct moments of time arise.

Returning to our two particle world, if we imagine the world-lines they have as shown in figure 1.25, we can see that partitioning them into Now Slices yields moments with matter-energy configurations that are distinguishable from one another.

Figure 1.25

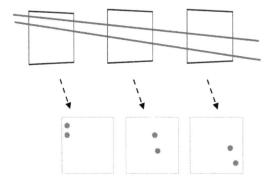

This is what moments are - individually distinct slices of the Spacetime block, as viewed from the perspective of a particular observer. The only sensible manner with which to label them, is with the 'timestamp' provided by their internal configuration.

The identity of any given moment then, is simply the things which it contains. The instants illustrated in figure 1.21 are not the labels 11:48:31, 11:48:32, and 11:48:33 - they are the little girls in the field. They are their smiles; their laughter; the sun in the sky; the wind in the grasses; and the shade of the trees. They are the tones of the sunlight kissing the Earth; the shadows that it casts; and the heat that it brings.

They are **my** moments, from my perspective. They are my Now Slices. They are the camera I hold; they are the little boy just out of shot; and they are the thoughts and emotions in our minds. They are everything that exists along those planes of simultaneity - every atom, field, and potential, stretching out from the Earth to the far reaches of the universe.

They are everlasting, and they are eternal. Yet while the romanticism of this provides a magical kind of comfort in the unending persistence of all things, it also presents us with a worrying conundrum with regards to cherished ideas such as free will, and our capacity for choice.

How can we possibly reconcile the notion that we are free to shape our own destinies, with the reality that we live in a world in which everything lasts forever, and is all already there across the fullness of time?

It is this troublesome, and often confusing issue, that we turn to next.

Free Will

&

The Sway of the Future

One of the deepest and most definitive aspects of our humanity, is our capacity for choice - our ability to choose. It resides at the very heart of our nature, forming the core of what we think of as ourselves, and shaping the way we conceive of our interactions with the world.

When faced with a fork in the road, we believe whole-heartedly we have the freedom of choice to select the path we will take. When I rise in the morning, I choose when I will shower... I choose to open the curtains and look out of the window... I choose which clothes I will wear... I choose to put my right foot before my left as I cross the landing and head for the stairs. I choose what I will eat for breakfast; whether I will read the paper or listen to the radio; whether I will rush for the early train; or whether I will move at my leisure.

I choose the manner in which I will behave when I arrive at work; which face I will show to people; whether I will act professionally; or whether I will shout at the top of my voice as I dance on the table claiming to be a chicken.

I choose... I choose.... I choose....

Yet if everything that is going to happen is pre-existing, just waiting for us to reach it in time (and is in fact even being lived-out as we speak by future versions of ourselves), then where does it leave us with regards to the notion of free will? How can we possibly claim to be in any sort of control of our lives if our paths - our 'destinies' - are already mapped out for us in a manner that is not only physically manifest, but unyielding to any form of change?

What choice do we actually have if our 'choices' are already made?

The moral issues raised by such a reality are frightening enough as of themselves. What of the man who cuts down another in cold-blooded murder? Is he to be excused because he had no choice? Was it not of his doing because his future was already determined?

And what of the one who comes to another's aid in an act of kindness? Should they not be praised for their actions because there was in fact no choice that was made?

Our rule of law and general moral code of right and wrong, are founded upon the idea that people are freely able to conduct themselves in the manner of their choosing. Who could say with a straight face that it would make no difference whatsoever if we were to abandon them, and leave ourselves open to a future free from the concepts of personal or collective responsibility? What do we think would happen if nobody felt so much as a shred of accountability for their actions?

I think I can safely suggest without too much dispute, that society would break down very quickly.

I - like most other people, I'm sure - feel with certainty that I am not swept along through the moments of my life a helpless passenger, stripped of any form of conscious choice as I robotically go through the motions of actions and decisions in which I have no say. On the contrary, I think, I assess, I choose, I act. I know it from the very core of my being, and yet, my future is already there.

We have already encountered three very deep philosophical questions posed to us by the true nature of the world (the questions of why we experience a flow of time that does not exist; whether or not we really are the single entities we imagine ourselves to be; and what is really meant by death when we live forever at each of our static Now Slices). This question of free will, presents the 4th such issue.

The laws of physics are very clear on the matter of how the universe is structured - that all events are pre-existing and stubbornly immutable to change, so how can we possibly square the experience of choice with the reality of a pre-written destiny?

The conclusion that is usually drawn by those who ponder this question of free will in a 4-dimensional world, is that as deeply as it may pain us - as deeply as it runs contrary to everything that we instinctively think of as making up our being - our perception of choice is but another deeply engrained illusion, conjured by the manner in which our minds interact with themselves.

There is a body of evidence from the field of neuroscience which suggests that at least in some circumstances, and in terms of choices being made by the conscious mind, that is in fact the case. Neural pathways responsible for motor control have been observed firing fractionally before the conscious mind 'chooses' to move a limb, for example. This would suggest that at least in some cases, the role of consciousness is as a post-event self-explanation engine.

Yet in spite of appearances, all is not lost.

Whether choices originate in the parts of the brain that give rise to consciousness, or whether they come from some deeper level, they do still originate from within the brain - from the locus of the thing that makes us, us. And with regards to the physics of time, the salvation of free will is to be found residing inherently within the nature of the Spacetime block itself - it's just that that nature is rather counter-intuitive to us, and does not automatically fall into line with our natural way of thinking.

This is because our world view is dominated by the illusion of a time which springs forth to carry us ever forwards along its relentless and unending current, while things move, change, and evolve with it as it seeps eternally from the void. This causes us to naturally think in terms of linear chains of events, and it is that way of thinking which trips us up, for it skews our interpretation of cause and effect, and leads us to worry about a loss of freedom due to a future that is already there.

Let's take a closer look at that statement, to see why -

In the Newtonian schema that rules our intuitions, cause and effect are a relatively simplistic affair, with cause always straight-forwardly and dependably preceding effect. Because of this, we tend to believe that explanations come in the form of starting conditions and events that subsequently act upon them. We are seduced by the illusion that it is the mechanical unfolding of linear chains of such events, which lead things to move from their initial conditions to an altered set of conditions which we like to term as the 'outcome'.

Things start off a certain way, things happen which cause them to change, and they subsequently end up being configured in a different way, right? - 'The stone is over there because it used to be here, and I picked it up and threw it, causing it to land over there'.

This is an example of the primacy we still naturally give to the past in terms of the explanations we create. But the erosion of what are perhaps some of the last remaining and most cherished vestiges of our instinctive notions of time, continues with the realisation that in a block universe, things cannot really work this way.

The truth of the matter is that the past, present, and future all exist simultaneously on an equal footing, and the past-directed bias in our explanations is introduced through the natural bias of our perspective. We formulate intuitions (and even so-called laws of motion) expressing dynamic change over time, precisely because that is the way in which we experience existence. We do not see the complete world-lines of the things in Spacetime, but instead discover their shapes one Now Slice at a time (via the mysterious 'flow' of time which we know cannot exist, yet we experience regardless). It is only natural then, that we think in terms of the dynamics we see, but it is important to understand that it's an illusion - the uncovering of world-lines one frame at a time leaves us not only with the false impression of motion, but the false impression that it is the combination of motion and starting conditions which together form the *cause* in our traditional views on cause and effect.

We assume motion to be the *explanation* as to why things become positioned the way that they are, for example, whereas strictly speaking, this is not really true.

In a block universe, the reasoning 'The stone is over there because it used to be here, and I picked it up and threw it, causing it to land over there', can be reformulated with greater validity as 'The stone was caused to follow a certain trajectory because it landed over there, and because it used to be here before I picked it up and threw it'.

Note that the concept of motion is transformed from *cause* to *effect* in this view, and the future state of the stone is a cause. This is a more valid perspective because the past and the future exist on an equal footing - they are both already there, and it is in fact the combination of both the initial and final conditions which conspire to cause the illusion of motion. It is the 'motion' that is the outcome - not the future position of the stone.

While this might seem like a strange way of talking (and we shall return to what it means for the concept of free will shortly), there is in fact an entire scheme of mechanics which works in precisely this manner. Intriguingly, in order to explain the motions of objects, it does not just simply *accommodate* the fact that the future is already there - it *requires* it...

It is an old idea, dating from 1788 when it was introduced by the Italian-French mathematician and astronomer Joseph-Louis Lagrange - 117 years before the advent of relativity and any sort of realisation that all of time exists all at once.

It is called 'Lagrangian Mechanics', or 'the Lagrangian Schema', and is based upon an idea called the 'principle of least action' which says that given a starting position at a certain point in time, and an ending position at a later point in time, then the path that an object traces between those two boundaries is the one which requires the least effort given any intervening obstacles and events. (When we talk of a 'path', we mean a trajectory through Spacetime - a 'history').

The great advantage of this approach over more traditional methods is that it is natively consistent with the reality of the block universe.

It works by treating Spacetime regions holistically in both the spatial and temporal dimensions. You first define the boundaries of the system (E.g. two points in space and time), and then describe how physical parameters are constrained over the bounded region as a whole. Then, for each possible set of events inside the region you calculate a value called the 'action', which involves the kinetic and potential energies of the system. The path constituting the string of events that have the lowest value of the action is the one that will occur (so the full paths are considered from end-to-end as though the entire journey happens all at once), and that's all there is to it - the path (the history) picked out by this method is the one that is the most economical in terms of energy expenditure over time.

Remarkably, the solutions which this simple yet counter-intuitive procedure gives, turn out to obey what we think of as the laws of motion!

That is to say, the laws of motion emerge quite naturally as a consequence of the fact that the universe will simply favour whatever is the most economical transition between any two given boundary states.

Newton's original laws of motion from the 1600's are in fact easily recoverable from the math, and arise naturally as an inevitable result of the tendency of the 'lazy universe' to minimise the effort required for a journey. All of classical physics, can in fact be expressed in terms of this principle of least action.

The fact that our familiar dynamical laws of physics derive from it, is suggestive that the Lagrangian schema penetrates a deeper level of meaning than that of mere mathematical convenience, and should be rightly considered a proper explanation of classical motion in a 4-dimensional world. Here, in the Lagrangian, we have the reason that the physical laws we find in nature are the way that they are.

The 'price' that you have to pay for accepting this, is that the very nature of how it works makes clear that the histories which we see play out, are in fact heavily influenced by *both* of the boundary conditions by which they are constrained. That is, history is the way it is, not only because of how it started, but also because of how it ends.

In order to obtain full explanations of what you witness in the present, you have to take into account things that happen 'in the future' - You have to look at the course of events holistically across the full duration of the time over which they play out, for the future wields a very real and physical influence over the past. It sculpts it, and shapes it into the reality that we find.

This is, of course, very much at odds with our everyday expectations - we naturally think in terms of the past affecting the future, but the notion of the future holding sway over the past is distinctly alien to our thinking. To help remedy this, it can be useful to think of explanations not in terms of causal chains of events running linearly from the past towards the future, but instead to choose to look upon them holistically in terms of Spacetime regions, and understand that they nest.

The Lagrangian schema, for example, can be used to examine a small region of Spacetime and obtain an explanation, before expanding the boundaries out such that they then encompass the original region. Since, as we have discussed, the contents of a Spacetime region can be explained in terms of its boundaries, then the new region can explain everything inside itself, including the original boundaries.

Figure 1.26

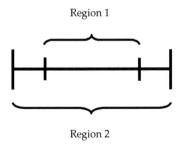

Region 1

Region 2

Treating the past and future in an even-handed manner such as this, where the full duration of events are considered all at once, leads to time-neutral explanations which are globally self-referential and self-consistent.

It is often objected that although using Lagrangian mechanics as the basis for calculation yields accurate results, it is uncomfortable to assign it any physical meaning because it seems to suggest a certain agency on behalf of the objects involved.

Take the case of a ray of light passing into a body of water, for example.

Figure 1.27

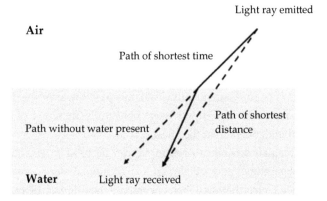

Light ray emitted

Air

Path of shortest time

Path of shortest distance

Path without water present

Water   Light ray received

Both the standard Newtonian and the Lagrangian approaches produce the same answer as to where the light travels and ends up, but offer differing explanations.

The Newtonian approach holds that it proceeds unimpeded until it hits the water and is diffracted by it, which alters its course and directs it to the point where it is received. Whereas the Lagrangian approach holds that the entire path (bend at the water's edge included) was selected from all other possibilities simply because it is quicker than the rest, given where the light must eventually end up. Light travels slower through water than it does through air, so choosing the path that has the optimal ratio of air-to-water, minimises the amount of energy that needs to be expended.

(The path of shortest distance is shown on the diagram to emphasize that the most direct route is not necessarily the one that requires the least action. Under the Lagrangian method, this path could have been taken but wasn't, simply because it has a greater value for the action).

Most people intuitively prefer the Newtonian approach because the Lagrangian way makes it sound a bit like it's saying the light took the path it did because it somehow 'knew' that it would be hitting the water before it set out.

But this is a misstep. There is no agency on behalf of the light. It isn't 'aware'. It doesn't foresee what its final destination is going to be, and somehow use that knowledge to make an informed decision about which is the most efficient path. It is simply that the future exists simultaneous with every other point in history, and given the constraint of its final (future) boundary, the light simply couldn't have taken any other route. It is self-consistent across its full duration.

The past is inseparably conjoined to the future. They shape and mold each other like the ocean and the ocean floor, and the nature of one affects the nature of the other in a beautiful and reciprocal interdependence that can never be broken.

Armed with this knowledge of how trajectories are caused as much by pre-existing future states as they are by events in the past and present, we can return to the question of free will, and see that our lives are like this too - they are self-consistent over all of our time. The fact that our futures are already there does not herald the death of free will, but instead means that we need to think about our future choices in the context of a reality obeying Lagrangian (rather than Newtonian) mechanics.

In such a world, while it is indeed useless to ask if we can alter the choices we will make tomorrow (for we cannot, because they **are** already made), we have to understand that they were made simultaneous with our past and present ones, and that it was nobody but future versions of **ourselves** who made them.

While it is true that they were not made in the strictly linear sequence that we might naturally imagine, and that when we 'arrive at them' in time they are 'already' made, that is not to say that they were made in the absence of free will. It is simply that our free will was exercised across all of them (individually) all at once. Collectively, they shape the trajectories of our lives, and should be thought of as causes (as opposed to future outcomes of current events), while the 'trajectories' (the 'paths') of the lives that we find, are the effect.

Understanding how to think about choice in a 4-dimensional world appears to restore free will to the picture, but we still need to give consideration to what a choice actually is. Sure - we can say that all choices happen at once (because all of time exists all at once), but are those choices *really* things in which we have a say?

It is often objected that because Spacetime is deterministic (that given the appropriate laws of motion, its evolution can be predicted from its starting conditions), the thought process in our brains can be nothing more than an inevitable series of events which come about as a result of purely bottom-up mechanical processes, in which we have no say. That is to say that the atoms of which our minds are constructed, evolve in a purely deterministic manner. In this view, choice is still an illusion, because our thoughts are determined by the application of the laws of physics to the starting conditions of the universe, and nothing more.

This though, is a mistake. It not only applies a Newtonian manner of thinking to the issue, but entirely misses the fact that a complex system such as a human being, while indeed being the product of a bottom-up process, also has the capacity to alter the physical situation in top-down manner. A consciousness is not only a product of the environment in which it is embedded, but is also capable of acting upon and altering that environment, and that needs to be taken into account.

Conscious systems make decisions, they select, they *choose*. When considering such systems (of which humanity is an example), it is more useful to think in terms of a bottom-up process that is coupled with top-down feedback. That feedback in turn contributes to and alters the bottom-up process.

Figure 1.28

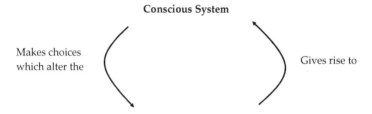

Conscious System

Makes choices
which alter the

Gives rise to

Deterministic Evolution of the Underlying Particles

The world-lines that such systems end up following, are caused as much by their conscious free will as they are by the conditions with which the universe began. Sentient beings are special patterns of matter, which are able to reflect upon themselves and pro-actively take action that alters the way a system would otherwise have evolved, and this has to be accounted for. It is an additional 'force' acting upon the underlying atoms.

It's a wonderful irony that in the end, one of the most troubling aspects of the nature of our world (the fact that at first glance our free will appears to be curtailed), should turn out to be one of its most beautiful things - that through the process of top-down feedback in a timeless objective whole, consciousness, and its capacity for freedom of choice, helped to shape the Everywhen.

Our futures may already be there, but it was none but ourselves who made them the way that they are.

Tomorrow's Now's still yet to be,

So shape the world of you and me,

In dawning's past,

The dream we found,

Was ever there,

In fate thus bound.

The Arrow of Time

&

The Problem of Flow

"In any attempt to bridge the domains of experience belonging to the spiritual and physical sides of nature, time occupies the key position"[6]

Arthur Eddington

The 'arrow of time' is the idea that there is a directionality, or 'asymmetry' to time. It is often confused with the concept of 'flow', but although they are ideas that are closely related, they are two very distinct issues - having a direction does not immediately imply a flow, and you could quite readily conceive of a flow which is lacking a consistent direction.

We know that there is no flow of time in the Everywhen, so the 'direction' we are speaking of here is the impression that our personal Now Slices seem to be ordered in such a way that they have a positive evolution - the next one consistently appears to be a forwards-in-time evolution of the state of the universe, rather than a backwards-in-time one.

If a mug of coffee is dropped to the floor, we would probably not be surprised to see it shatter into many pieces, with the coffee being spilled and splattered up the walls. It would however, be more than a little surprising to us if a few seconds later, it were to peel itself off the walls and pour back into the spontaneously re-assembling mug, before jumping back into our waiting hand - this sort of thing tends not to happen.

This is curious though, as the laws of physics work just as well in the backwards direction of time as they do in the forwards one. The laws of motion which govern how the individual atoms of the coffee mug behave, for example, are completely agnostic of any 'direction' of time, and do not prevent such a thing from happening. If you were able to view a movie shot at the microscopic level showing the individual atoms moving, colliding, and rebounding, it would look just as plausible played either forwards or backwards. All the energies, masses, and momenta involved work out perfectly well in either temporal direction.

At the atomic level, time seems to be symmetric. So why do we not see things such as smashed coffee mugs spontaneously re-assembling? Why is it, that at the macroscopic level of everyday objects, we experience a uniquely forwards direction of time?

The British astronomer Arthur Eddington was puzzling over this question in 1927, when he realised there was a correlation between the way the entropy of a system evolves, and the direction of time. Entropy is the measure of disorder there is in a system.

Imagine the individual molecules of gas contained in a some sort of jar. Let's say that they all happen to be congregated in one corner, and arranged into neat rows.

Figure 1.29

This state is highly ordered, so we say it has low entropy. If we look at all of the possible positions that each molecule may take on in the next snapshot, then the overwhelming majority of possible configurations will result in an overall picture that is slightly less ordered. There are a very small number of overall configurations that are more ordered, but they require each molecule to move in just the right way so that overall they become packed into neat rows with less space between them. So while it is entirely feasible that some individual molecules may indeed happen to move in that way, the more of them there are, the less likely it becomes that they **all** happen to do so.

In a typical situation involving billions of molecules, there are a great many configurations that the gas can potentially take on within the tank, and from a starting position of high order, it is overwhelmingly more likely that the next state will be more highly disordered.

This is known as the 2nd law of thermodynamics, or more commonly, as simply 'the 2nd law'. It is an 'emergent' law, in that it is not explicitly encoded into any of the many constituent parts of the system, but when those individual parts interact, then it faithfully describes how they behave as a whole.

This idea of emergence is important, and will prove to be critical to our understanding of the world in later chapters, so it's worth pausing for a second to elaborate a little further.

The majority of complex systems in fact display some degree of emergence, and are subject to laws which apply at the level of the system, rather than at the level of the components from which they are made. In such systems, it is often more useful to consider those system-level laws than those that operate at the level of the microphysics beneath. Theories, and fields of knowledge, sit on top of each other at different levels of abstraction - Physics sits atop physical reality, chemistry sits atop physics, biology atop chemistry, etc. etc. Further up the chain somewhere is zoology, and further still is psychology, economics, and a whole host of others.

You choose the level of abstraction appropriate to the questions you are seeking to address, because theories that operate at the appropriate level of abstraction often hold more relevant explanatory power. Working out what is likely to happen when a hungry snake and a mouse are placed together in a box, is one example of this. In this particular case, you would perhaps use zoology rather than atomic electrodynamics, for example). Working out the manner in which a gas spreads in a container is another, and in this case, we turn to the 2nd law of thermodynamics.

It states that the total entropy (disorder) of a closed system increases over time, and is actually applicable to **any** closed system. When that closed system is taken to be the universe as a whole, then its 'starting condition' - the state in which it 'began' - is taken to be a boundary point of minimal entropy, from which disorder increases as you move further away from it in time.

As there are an unimaginably high number of particles in the universe, we can assume with near certainty that whatever the 'next' state is, it will be more disordered than the 'current' one.

This is known as the 'thermodynamic arrow of time', and is often cited as the cause of our seemingly unstoppable march into the future. This however, is a bit misleading. What it actually amounts to is an explanation of ordering - **not** of flow. For now, we should satisfy ourselves with the weaker assertion that there is a correlation between the amount of disorder there is in a system, and the amount of time over which it has evolved.

The fact that more entropy is all but guaranteed in future Now Slices is symptomatic of our current location in the Everywhen. I.e. we are located in a place where the universe has not yet reached thermal equilibrium (maximum entropy).

Assuming that our best theories for the topology of the universe are correct, then approximately 10^{106} years from now, it is anticipated that the state of thermal equilibrium will have been reached. This is a time where all of the temperature gradients in the universe will have been evened out, and there is no thermodynamic free energy. I.e. The state of the universe is perfectly disordered, and there is no longer any change that can possibly bring about an increase in entropy.

This is often referred to as the 'Heat Death' of the universe. In such a state, all of the energy that was bound up in matter has been converted to heat, and dissipated smoothly throughout the cosmos. That cosmos has expanded to such an extent, that it has cooled to a point there is no longer enough energy left to do any work. The universe consists of fundamental particles spread so thinly as to be negligible, and all motion has ceased.

It was not always thought that this would be the case - For many years, it was assumed that instead of expanding endlessly into a cold death, the universe would in fact reach a point where it began contracting under the gravity of its contents. A positive cosmological constant though - a mysterious force called 'Dark Energy' - appears to be accelerating the expansion of the universe. We now know that it will continue to push things further and further apart, until eventually, all things will have broken down into their constituent atoms. Those atoms will be separated by great distances from each other, and heat-death will ensue.

But to return to the central question with which we are concerned - why do we experience any movement towards the future at all? The thermodynamic arrow of time approximates our direction, but is not responsible for any sensation of flow. As we have seen, an entirely static Spacetime block presents a significant challenge in reconciling the manner in which we experience the world, with the way that the laws of physics tell us it must be.

If those laws neither allow for time itself to flow, nor for us to move through it along our world-lines, then how is it that we feel so surely the passage of time?

The answer that is usually offered to this deepest of questions, is the same as was previously presented to explain why we feel as though we are each a single entity. I.e. that it is because at each Now Slice, we posses a brain that is encoded with memories of the past, giving us the impression that we have experienced previous moments.

This answer though, can only account for part of the story (the impression that we have a past - a history), and is wholly inadequate as a complete and robust answer to the question of why we experience the sensation of 'flow'.

There are at least two major issues that it leaves unaddressed:

1)   If memory genuinely accounted for the whole story, then surely we would have the experience of being 'stuck' against the im-moveable wall of a single moment, enduringly trapped to stare into the memory of the past, and yet we do not. We instead have the perception of a forwards motion. It is not that we simply have the memories of previous moments - we have the constant experience of new ones replacing the current as we transition forwards, and memory alone cannot fully account for this.

2)   In an entirely static 4-dimensional reality, we are in need of a jus-
tification as to how and why we are able to think; to perceive; and
to contemplate the past that we are supposedly reflecting upon in
perpetuity.

There are no Now Slices in which the electrical signals that
underlie our thought processes are anything other than frozen in
time too - just like everything else. There should therefore be no
person anywhere, whose mind is anything other than inert, life-
less, and entirely devoid of awareness, because the electrons in
their brains are not moving. So if they are incapable of having so
much as a single thought, then how exactly do we suppose it   is
the very thought processes of   memory which are solely responsible for our   delusion of time's flow? It is a circular argument
which makes no sense.

These points are not intended as a criticism of the block universe - on the
contrary, they are intended to highlight the need for an adequate
explanatory framework to sit atop it. We are, in my view, missing an
elucidatory layer which is capable of answering the essential questions laid
out above. We are missing the magic ingredient that gives the world its
subjective dynamism; its flow. If that thing cannot be a flow of time, and it
cannot be a flow through time, then it must be something else - some other
mechanism - for else none of us has ever so much as had the privilege to
conjure but a single thought.

There have been attempts to put forward alternate views - one's other
than that of the block universe, in order to restore the flow of time and avoid
troublesome questions such as these. They have all failed, for only a fully
realized static Spacetime block is compatible with Einstein's Relativity.

A theory called the 'Growing Block Universe', was an example of one
such attempt. It featured a partial adoption of the block view, in which the
past persists eternally, but the future does not have any reality until it is
brought into being by an ever-advancing and universal present moment. We
could simply point out that it used a Newtonian view of time (I.e. a single
universal Now that is shared by all), and leave it at that, but the
philosophers Braddon-Mitchell, Bourne, and Merricks go on to highlight

that it fails to accomplish its goals regardless - anyone who is located in any part of the block other than the growing present, finds themselves in the exact same situation as in the standard view. So even if it worked, it would be unclear how it really helps.

The answer to this most mesmerizing of questions then, is not to be found in modifying the block universe. It must instead be found residing inherently within it.

The question of flow, goes straight to the very heart of what it is to experience life. Our bodies are confined to many singular and frozen instants of time, and yet it would seem that our minds - our conscious experiences, are somehow not. As outrageous as it might be, and make no mistake - it is surely the strangest and most miraculous thing that there is - we do perceive, and our minds are a-buzz with the fervour of conscious thought.

The great question, is with regards to how that can possibly be... Why can we think? And why do those thought processes leave us with an impression of a time which is flowing, when we know beyond all doubt that it is not?

Conscious we see,

Yet how can we know?

If static in time,

Without any flow?

Time, for all the familiarity with which we thought we knew it, is not what it seems. The world is a 4-dimensional landscape in which nothing truly moves, and nothing ever changes.

There are many deep and philosophical questions posed by this, all of which have their roots in the fact that all of time just is. We have explored some of them here, and in cases such as the eternal nature of all things, and the question of free will in a world where the future is already there, we have found the kind of strange and unexpected resolution that we can probably just about come to terms with and accept. Other questions, such as the ones of what exactly the 'I' in each of us is, when there are many versions of us living concurrent with ourselves; how we are able to think if those versions are all just static 'snapshots'; and why on earth we should experience a subjective flow of time when the world is resolutely still, remain stubbornly and enigmatically out of reach.

It is these questions in particular - the one's which remain shrouded in mystery, which the remainder of this book is dedicated to exploring. What are we? Why are we aware? And how do we experience a motion through time when such a thing isn't really there? Everything that is covered from this point onwards, is done so with the resolution of these (perhaps connected?) issues in mind.

A fools errand? Perhaps. But to reiterate the words with which I opened - 'The quest for knowledge is the unquenchable thirst of the human soul... It is the desire to know the world in which we live; to glimpse the wiring under the board; and ultimately to know ourselves, that we might better understand our place in the cosmos, who we are, and what (if anything), that might mean'.

The road may be lit dimly, and its labyrinthine routes may sprawl into the darkness of the night, but it is the insatiable allure of the unknown which impels us to try...

In search of answers then, we turn in hope to the remarkable world of the quantum...

II - The Quantum

*"My own suspicion is that the universe is not only queerer than we suppose, but queerer than we **can** suppose [...] I Suspect that there are more things in heaven and earth than are dreamed of, or can be dreamed of, in any philosophy."*[7]

J. B. S. Haldane

The Strangeness of Light

&

The Nature of Matter

"When it comes to atoms, language can be used only as in poetry"[8]

Niels Bohr

Relativity is a theory of the classical realm, and has thrown up a deep and puzzling mystery regarding the flow of time. The underpinnings of that classical realm though, are quantum mechanical by nature. The world with which we are familiar (even once Relativity has been accounted for), is an approximation that emerges from the enigmatic and esoteric world of the quantum - a world which contains wonders so peculiar as to bring to mind the prophetical words of Haldane, and his famous musing that the universe may be stranger than we are even able to conceive.

Yet while the deep underpinnings of existence **are** distinctly alien by way of contrast to our everyday experience, with regards to quantum mechanics at least, there **are** understandings within our grasp. (Though admittedly, they are rather surprising, for sure).

We, as human beings, are used to dealing with the classical approximation. We are macro-scale objects, and our minds are attuned to dealing with the world at that scale. Just as the fact that we move largely at everyday speeds deceives us into the false belief in a universal present moment, so our familiarity with the macro-scale classical approximation of the world causes us to find the workings of quantum theory so bizarre. But in order to find the answers we seek, it is necessary to take a deep breath and plunge the depths of that weird and wonderful rabbit hole.

The difficulties of providing an explanation for what we find there, has lead to a host of different 'interpretations' of what it implies for the nature of reality. There is just one quantum theory. It is the same one that is used to make calculations and predictions by all, and in terms of its predictive power, it is the single most successful theory of all time - the crowning jewel in our glittering and ever-growing body of knowledge. But perhaps because of its inherently counter-intuitive nature, there are numerous competing ideas with regards to what it must *mean*. In order to successfully navigate them, it is helpful to first start at the beginning -

A 'quantum' is a discreet amount of something - a quantity. Quantum theory is the realisation that the things of which the world is composed, are quantised. That is to say that the world is not smooth, but discontinuous and granular. Even things such as energy and light come in discreet indivisible chunks which we call 'quanta', and they behave in some very unexpected ways.

The story begins in earnest with Albert Einstein, in the inauspicious confines of the Swiss patent office, in what has become known as 'the year of miracles' - 1905. For someone who was at the time not actually working as a physicist, but as a patents clerk, Einstein was having one hell of a year… In addition to his seminal paper on Special Relativity, he was to also produce pivotal works on Brownian motion (which lead to the discovery of atoms), the relation between mass and energy (perhaps the most famous equation of all time - $E=MC^2$), and crucially, the 'photoelectric effect'. The Nobel prize could rightfully have been awarded for any one of those things, and indeed, there is an argument that he could have received four for his work in that year alone, for between them, those papers were to radically change our view of reality. But it was his ideas on the photoelectric effect that were to win Einstein the prize. It was this paper that was to go on to kick-off the quantum revolution, and though he did not realise it at the time, that revolution would ultimately harbour surprises even more shocking than those which arise from Relativity.

The photoelectric effect is essentially the process by which, under the right circumstances, electrons are freed from the surface of a solid when it is illuminated with a beam of light. It is the magic that enables our modern-day light sensors to control things like automatic doors, for example. It had first been observed by Heinrich Hertz in 1887, but presented something of a mystery. It is caused by the transfer of energy from the light to the electrons which it strikes. The additional energy the electrons receive allows them to escape (and, for example, flow around an electrical circuit and make an automatic door open or close). This was understood, but there was something strange at play - the intensity of the light appeared to play little role.

Electrons exposed to very bright light were ejected with the same energies as those exposed to very dim light. The only thing that the intensity of the beam seemed to have an influence over, was the quantity of electrons affected. This was curious, and ran contrary to the understanding of physics that existed at the time. It had been expected that the brighter the light, the more energetic the ejected electrons would be.

This expectation was due largely to the established school of thought, which held that light was an electromagnetic wave. At the end of the nineteenth century, there was little doubt about the validity and completeness of this view. The wave-like nature of light had been long-since confirmed by a famous experiment performed by Thomas Young in 1801.

Young set up his experiment to settle a long-standing debate over whether light was a stream of particles (as conceived by Sir Isaac Newton), or a wave (as conceived by Christiaan Huygens). He used a light source which he directed at a screen, with a barrier containing two thin slits placed between the source and the screen.

Figure 2.1

Detection Screen

The idea was that if light were a stream of particles, then you would get two bright parallel lines showing up on the screen, in line with where the particles had passed through the double slits.

Figure 2.2

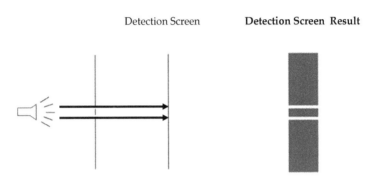

Detection Screen   **Detection Screen Result**

Whereas, if light were a wave, you should expect to see a diffraction pattern on the screen, where the wave had passed through both slits, generating two 'new' waves that interfered with each other, producing a series of light and dark bands at the screen.

Figure 2.3

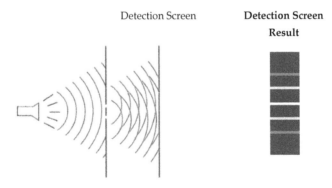

Detection Screen   **Detection Screen Result**

The result of the experiment showed very clearly the diffraction pattern consistent with the detection of a wave.

The concept of light as a wave was thereafter routinely applied to successfully explain a wide range of optical phenomena, including reflection, refraction, interference, polarization, and diffraction.

In the case of the photoelectric effect, the situation was visualised as something analogous to electrons being anchored in the solid, amid a sea of electromagnetic radiation, with light being the waves in that radiation. As such, one would expect that weak waves (low intensity light) might have little effect, and that high-energy waves (high intensity light) would more readily dislodge an electron. But this is not what happens.

Instead, tiny ripples in an otherwise calm sea, while leaving most electrons untouched, can suddenly affect one in such a manner that it is rocketed away from the solid in which it is anchored. Furthermore, while the intensity of the light appeared to have little relevance, its *colour* did! Light of a certain colour would make electrons break free regardless of the intensity of the beam, whereas light of a different colour would not.

Given this, it was clear that something was amiss in our understanding. Meanwhile, Max Planck had been struggling with a related mystery surrounding something called 'black-body radiation', which is about how heat is radiated from an object. The difficulty he was grappling with, was that experimental results didn't match with theory when it came to ultra-violet light. A certain behaviour was predicted, but a very different one was observed.

After much tribulation, and in what he described as an act of desperation, he introduced the seemingly arbitrary postulation that standing-waves inside an object can only assume discreet energy values. I.e. that the energy levels of such waves are quantised, as opposed to being smooth and continuous (as the understanding of the day had been). This allowed him to produce a formula that successfully modelled the distribution of the radiation intensity that was observed through experiment.

Although he had found a mathematical model which worked, he did not view it as being a real-world description of what was actually happening. He instead thought of it more as a mathematical slight-of-hand that just so happened to fit with observation. This was because packaging light into energy quanta carried with it the implication that it was a stream of particles, rather than a wave, which seemed absurd given what was known at the time regarding the nature of light.

What Einstein did, was to recognise that Planck's mathematical contrivance could in fact be taken as a reasonable description of reality, and applied the same sort of thinking to the problem of the photoelectric effect.

He reasoned that if we thought of light not as a wave, but as a stream of discreet energy 'quanta' (particles), then the mystery surrounding the behaviour of electrons in the photoelectric effect could be resolved.

It is these light quanta that would later become known as 'photons'.
Einstein had realised that if a particle of light - a photon - oscillated with just the right frequency (and this point is crucial, for as frequency determines colour, it explains why it takes light of a certain colour to make an electron break free), then it could transfer the energy of that oscillation to the electron which it strikes, and make it 'jump'. It is the frequency of the individual particles of light which matters - not the intensity of the light. All the intensity does is dictate how many individual particles there are. Raising that intensity might make it more likely that an electron receives a direct hit, but unless the colour of the light is right, it won't make any difference.

To borrow a metaphor from the physicist Carlo Rovelli, it is a bit like a hailstorm hitting your car - if the individual hailstones are not big enough, then the intensity of the shower doesn't matter... your car isn't going to get dented. But if those hailstones **are** big enough, then it will.

And with this, the mystery of the photoelectric effect could be explained, but it came with a troublesome price - you had to accept that light is made of particles; that it has a granularity.

The difficulty here was that in addition to a significant body of experimental evidence already confirming light to be a wave, there was now equally valid evidence to instead suggest it to be made of particles. Nothing is ever straight-forwards...

The debate that ensued over which view is correct, was not able to be resolved one way or the other, for as it turns out, both accounts are true. It is almost as though there are many particles collectively behaving in a wave-like manner - bumping and jostling each other into the interference pattern seen in Young's double slit experiment, and it might be tempting to conclude that it really is that simple, and that's all that's going on. Repeating the experiment with just one photon at a time though, reveals that this cannot be the case. Incredibly, if you take great care to ensure that only one photon at a time is fired through the slits, they each still follow the path of a wave, and the interference pattern is built-up on the detection screen one photon at a time!

Figure 2.4

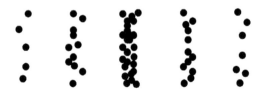

Each photon **still** behaves as though it is being bumped and jostled by many others - even though it is the only one that can be seen to be present. So if it's the only photon that's there, then what exactly, is it being driven off-course by? What is interfering with it?

It is as though the individual photons each travel through **both** slits like they are waves, and interfere with **themselves** before registering as particles (so not waves after all then?) when they strike the detection screen.

The photon, it would seem, cannot be fully described by either the wave or particle views alone - only by both. This is known as the wave-particle duality of light, and was the first true glimpse into the remarkable world of the quantum. Einstein's great insight was that Planck's mathematical conjuring trick, far from being the abstract tool it was thought to have been, was in fact under the correct circumstances, an actual description of physical reality - In situations where it is propagating, light behaves as a wave, and in situations where it is being either emitted or absorbed, it behaves like a particle. I want to make a point of emphasizing the importance of this, for it will eventually prove to be of great importance to us in a fascinating aspect of our understanding of time - a single photon interferes with itself as though there are many others present, when in fact there are not.

This marks the true beginnings of quantum mechanics. It was from here that the revolution really began, and as bizarre as this result was, things were about to get even stranger. For incredibly, and against (almost) all expectation, it wasn't only the light...

Believing there exist inherent symmetries in the laws of physics, in 1924 the French nobleman Louis de Broglie published his doctorial dissertation, setting out the hypothesis that if light could behave as both a particle and a wave, then perhaps matter could too.

Although at odds with intuition, this was less far-fetched than it first sounds. The classic vision of the atom (the same one that you were probably taught in school) is a bit like a mini solar system, with electrons orbiting the nucleus in much the same manner as the planets orbit the Sun.

Figure 2.5

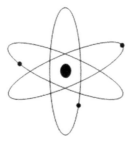

This simple and orderly picture though, was known to have certain difficulties. One was the question of why the electrons could only seem to take certain orbits, and another was why on Earth they were stable. Everything that was known about mechanics at the time, suggested that they ought to spiral inwards and crash into the nucleus within a fraction of a second, but this obviously didn't happen.

Niels Bohr had already answered these questions with a new and updated model of the atom, and within that model, there were echoes of the quantisation of light.

The orbits of electrons are their energy levels. The closer they are to the nucleus, the less energy they have. This was already understood. Bohr had realised that if we treated electrons less like little planets, and more like waves, then the overall picture started to make more sense. He imagined an electron in orbit around a nucleus as being a standing-wave, and from this it was clear that the frequency of that wave corresponded to its energy. That is, an electron's frequency determines its orbit, and as frequencies of standing-waves can clearly only come in whole numbers, then only certain discreet (quantised) orbits could be permitted.

Figure 2.6

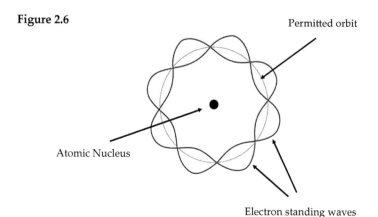

Permitted orbit

Atomic Nucleus

Electron standing waves

This paralleled the situation with the discreet energy values of the standing waves in Max Planck's model of thermal radiation, and so De Broglie's thesis centred around the observation that since light and matter are both quantised, then maybe the dualistic properties of light would be translated to matter too.

If he were correct, then it would mean that the foundations of our very reality - the foundations we had always assumed to be inherently solid and substantial by nature - would in fact turn out to be just as strange and ethereal as light.

Some years later, this was in fact shown to be the case.

The famed double-slit experiment was repeated, this time not with quanta of light, but with electrons. In a setup which echoed that of Young's original experiment, electrons were fired from a source onto a detection screen, passing through a barrier which lay between. As in Young's experiment, that barrier contained two narrow slits, and the detection of an interference pattern at the screen would indicate the electrons had behaved as a wave, whereas a pair of narrow bands would indicate only particle-like behaviour.

Remarkably, it was the interference pattern that was detected, and just as it was with the light, the result persisted when electrons were fired towards the screen just one at a time. Ordinary matter, it would seem, has wave-like properties too, and in a double slit experiment, behaves just the same as light.

Figure 2.7

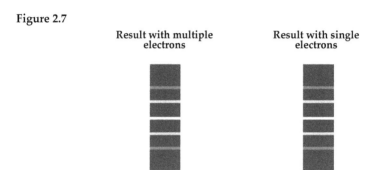

Baffled by how a solid piece of matter can possibly pass through both slits at the same time, and interfere with itself before registering at the detection screen as a solid particle, physicists wanted to take a closer look at exactly what was happening at the slits.

So the experiment was repeated again, except this time with additional detection apparatus located at the slits, so that it could be observed whether the individual electrons really were passing through both of them or not (and if so, just exactly what that might actually look like!)

Figure 2.8

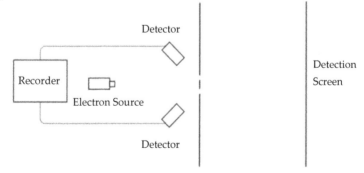

And now, something truly extraordinary happened…

The electrons were observed passing through just one slit or the other - explicitly **not** both. However, with the introduction of the detection apparatus at the slits, the interference pattern was no longer found at the detection screen - it was instead replaced with the pair of narrow bands consistent with particle-like behaviour! The introduction of the additional detection equipment had changed the outcome of the experiment...

Figure 2.9

Result with slit detectors active

If the slit detectors were turned off, then the electrons went back to passing through the slits as waves, until they hit the screen and 'became' particles there. If the detectors were turned back on, the electrons 'became' particles before they reached the slits, and then went through just one slit or the other.

If the slit detectors were taken slightly out of focus, then some of the electrons 'became' particles before they passed through the slits, and others only did so when they reached the screen.

The very act of observing what the electrons were doing, was changing how they behaved...

The experiment has been repeated many times, both with matter and with light, and the results are always consistent. Whether we are talking about light or matter, both display a wave-particle duality, and both behave as a wave until they are 'observed', or 'measured' (in the example of the double slit experiment, detection at either the detection screen or via recording equipment placed at the slits, constitutes a measurement), at which point they become a particle.

How could the act of simply measuring them convert them from a wave to a particle? The answer to this question will be of great importance to us. For now though, we shall content ourselves with the fact that this result confirmed De Broglie's hypothesis, and demonstrated conclusively the existence of matter waves. All matter is characterised by this - everything from an electron to a planet (and more). You; me; the mountains; the rivers; your house; your car; your dog; the Earth; the Moon; the Sun; the galaxy... everything and anything that is constructed of atoms consists of this strange duality, whereby it can exhibit either particle-like or wave-like behaviour. The wavelength of such matter waves (or 'De Broglie waves') is known as the 'De Broglie wavelength'.

So why do we not see wave-like phenomena at the scale of classical objects? Why should it be only confined to the realm of particles? We do not diffract and become spread-out when we pass through a doorway (thankfully...), and we certainly do not seem to pass through multiple doorways at once... We do not merge into one another and interfere like waves when we make physical contact, and yet if we ourselves have this wave-particle duality, then why not?

The answer lies in the incredibly short wavelengths that macro-scale objects (such as cars, planets, and ourselves) have compared to their size (their energy). The De Broglie wavelength of an object is inversely proportional to its mass. I.e. the greater the mass, the shorter the wavelength. In order for the wave-like behaviour of a system (such as a person, for example) to be noticeable, its wavelength needs to be comparable to its size.

A typical grain of sand might have a wavelength one trillionth of the size of an atomic nucleus, so its wave-like properties are not observable. If you consider even larger objects, such as people, you can quickly see that their wavelengths will be absolutely miniscule, and to all intents and purposes insignificant. This is the reason that we do not observe macro-scale objects behaving like waves - the behaviour is there, it's just so indiscernible as to be immaterial. In the case of the electron however, with its diminutive mass, the De Broglie wavelength is larger than the electron itself, and so its wave-like behaviours are dominant.

With the fundamental building blocks of matter obeying wave-like behaviour, and with so little being understood about the processes underlying it, the quest was on to describe the mysterious duality that reigns over the stuff of which we are made...

In freedom friend,

I'll spread myself broadly,

But should we relate,

I shall strike thee as whole...

Superposition

With things that had been thought of as fundamentally 'wavey' behaving like particles, and things that had been considered fundamentally solid behaving like waves, we were in desperate need of a new explanatory framework. So in the pursuit of a reconciliation of this strange duality, the physicists Erwin Schrödinger and Max Born conceptualised photons as being particles which obeyed a probability wave (or 'wave function').

This abstract mathematical construct, they postulated, dictated the probabilities that the various variables associated with a particle would take particular values - variables such as its position, momentum, etc.

Schrödinger devised an ingenious formula - the wave equation - to describe it, and Born demonstrated that, when measuring a particle's position for example, the probability of finding it at any particular location was related to the square of the amplitude of the abstract wave at that point.

So while an individual quanta of light is propagating through a double slit experiment, for example, it should behave as though it's moving as part of a wave, until it is measured. The actual quanta itself could be located anywhere within that wave, and the chances of actually finding it at any particular point is given by what became known as the 'Born rule' (squaring the amplitude of the wave at that point).

Figure 2.11

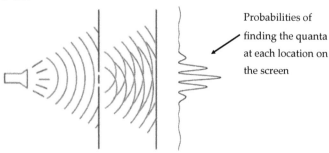

Probabilities of
finding the quanta
at each location on
the screen

The predictions made by the math tallied perfectly with observation, accurately reproducing the density of photon strikes on the screen through the projected probabilities.

And it was applicable to the distribution of electrons around the atom too. Schrödinger worked out the precise solutions of the wave equation for the hydrogen atom, and the results were in perfect agreement with observation.

His equation, as it turns out, is applicable to **all** matter (and all EM radiation), and provides a means by which to determine the probability of finding any particle at any given location in space and time. While not explicitly offering an explanation of what's going on in the fundamental reality, it provides a powerful predictive tool that is among the most important discoveries in the history of science. His method of calculation became known as 'wave mechanics'.

But what are we to make of this so-called wave of probabilities? Is it simply a convenient mathematical construct that just so happens to give exquisitely accurate results, or does it represent something physical? Wave mechanics makes no assertion one way or the other, but it's a critically important point, so let's examine the nature of the wave function a little deeper -

The fact that the motions of individual particles can be described in accordance with a wave function is fascinating (and is at the heart of the so-called wave-particle duality), for in the probability wave, at each time-step a particle takes every possible value for a variable that it can, all at the same time. In the example of the double slits, if we look at the 'position' variable, it's like each individual photon is in each of its potential positions all at once.

I.e. it's like there are many different versions of what the reality of the situation could be, and they are all superposed on top of each other in chorus. This is a crucially important feature of the quantum world, and will prove to be of great significance to us in our understanding of time. It is something we refer to as the 'quantum superposition'.

A superposition is the overall quantum state of something, which is composed of multiple alternate states (called 'eigenstates') of that same thing. In the example of our photon, let's say that while it is travelling (I.e. in its wave-like mode) then it could be in positions x, y, or z in accordance with the wave function at a particular time-step (for simplicity let's imagine that it could only be in these three positions... the reality is more akin to trillions....). So its eigenstates with regards to its position are x, y, and z, and it has an overall superposition of x + y + z. The three alternative positions are all superposed on top of each other, something like as shown in figure 2.12.

Figure 2.12

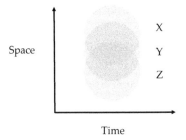

Space
X
Y
Z

Time

Between measurements, according to wave mechanics, the photon is not in any one position x, y, or z - it is in a superposition of all of them. It is only when a measurement occurs, that we see it adopt any one particular eigenstate, and which one that is, is governed probabilistically by the Born rule.

Working in parallel to Schrödinger and Born was another physicist by the name of Werner Heisenberg, who independently developed a different method of predicting the same outcomes of quantum phenomena, and in fact delivered it to the world a year earlier. His method was called 'matrix mechanics', and used an obscure mathematics that was unfamiliar to most other physicists of the day. Perhaps for this reason, it was Schrödinger's method that caught-on (physicists being already familiar with the concept of waves).

Matrix mechanics though, more readily illuminates a fascinating tension between pairs of 'complementary' observable properties of particles. These special pairings of properties, revealed that what had previously been assumed to be independent features of reality, were in fact deeply connected.

We have so far used the example of the 'position' property, so let's stick with that for now. It turns out, that position is paired with momentum, and they are in fact just different aspects of the same underlying thing.

It had always been thought, for example, that we ought to be able to determine the current position of something, as well as the momentum with which it is moving. Remarkably, for particles this is not so. Even more remarkably, the reason for this is because if it has a sharply defined value for one of those things, then it inherently cannot have a sharply defined value for the other.

It is as if the position-momentum dichotomy of a particle exists on a sliding scale between the two things.

In figure 2.10, Point A represents a situation where the particle has a sharply defined position. Note that this is also the point where the momentum is least well defined. Point B is the opposite - it is where the momentum is clear, but the position is at its most fuzzy. Point C is somewhere in between, where both properties are kind of roughly defined.

Figure 2.10

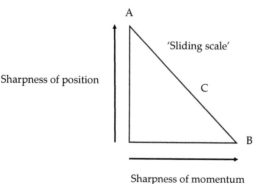

A particle cannot have position and momentum independent of one another - it can only adopt a place somewhere along the sliding scale between both.

This is Heisenberg's famous Uncertainty Principle. If there is a clear value for one property, then the other is by definition in a superposition of all the possible values that it could have. In fact it goes further - obtaining a value for one observable of a complementary pair, actually seems to destroy any previous value that was there for the other, replacing it with a superposition.

It's like a frayed string which stubbornly refuses to be pinched into a point at both ends at once.

Figure 2.13

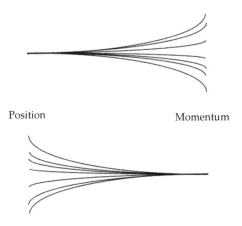

Position   Momentum

You can pinch it at one end or the other, but never both. This can be shown very nicely through experiment. The typical example involves a different pair of complementary observables - the particle's spin along two different axes. Spin is a confusing property though (it's not what it sounds like), so for the sake of illustration, it's customary to replace it with some other arbitrary properties, such as 'colour' and 'hardness', which for purpose of the example, we shall take to be complementary.

Suppose we measure an electron as being colour 'white'. Once we know what the colour is, we can then go on to measure it as many times as we like, and it will continue to come up white. If we then measure its hardness, we might determine it to be 'soft'. So we might go on to conclude that the electron is both soft and white. But we would be mistaken. Having measured its hardness, the next measurement of its colour *might* come up white, or it might not. Let's take a look at what's happening -

When we first measure the colour, we get a definite value for it, which consequently places its 'hardness' into a superposition. Our next measurements of colour all come up white, because the electron is white. But when we measure its hardness, we obtain a definite value for that property, which places its colour back into a superposition. It is no longer white. When we next measure the colour, it takes on the value of one of the colour superposition eigenstates, which might be white, or might not be.

This is true of any pairs of complementary variables - you can only ever know the value of one of them, as knowing one guarantees that the other is in a superposition.

In 1926, Schrödinger published a mathematical proof which demonstrated that his wave mechanics and Heisenberg's matrix mechanics were in fact equivalent, revealing them to simply be different representations of the same theory. That theory, was to become known as 'quantum mechanics'.

So where exactly does all of this leave us? How precisely are we to interpret this strange concept of superposition? What does it represent? The way it evolves over time is described by the wave function, but just what is it that is supposed to be 'waving'? Does it have a physicality? Or is it just a fancy tool we use to handle the statistics? And what actually happens when we make an observation? How does simply looking at what a particle is doing end up replacing a superposition with a definitive value?

These are deep and divisive questions, which to this day have no universally agreed consensus (and this is where the various different 'interpretations' of quantum mechanics come from), but in 1927 the greatest minds in physics came together to try and hammer it out at the now famous 5th Solvay Conference in Brussels.

Amongst their number were Einstein, Bohr, Heisenberg, Schrödinger, Born, De Broglie, Lorentz, Dirac, Curie, and Planck. A heady bunch by any stretch. No less than seventeen of the attendees either already were, or went on to become, Nobel Prize winners.

What they came up with (not unanimously, it must be said), was the famed 'Copenhagen Interpretation', so named due to the fact of it being the brainchild of Niels Bohr, who was based in Copenhagen.

This was the first of many such 'interpretations', and if you've ever been taught quantum mechanics, it's likely to have been this interpretation you were shown. The world-view it lays out is essentially that the superposition is unphysical, and is representative only of the possible states that may or may not manifest as reality if an observation were to happen.

This means that left to their own devices, particles exist only as a cloud of probabilities which evolve in accordance with the wave equation. Under these circumstances, they posses no physical properties - just the potential to adopt them. In essence, they have no physical existence.

But this is not their only mode of operation - under the Copenhagen interpretation, there is an abrupt disjunction between the way a particle behaves when it is left alone, and the way it behaves while under observation. When observed, its natural adherence to the evolution of the wave equation is suddenly broken, and the probability wave instantaneously 'collapses' down onto a single value selected at random (but in accordance with the prescribed probabilities). It is then, and only then, that the particle actually has any physical properties. Between observations, it is as a spectre - a whisper on the breeze that isn't really there.

While it is quite obvious why this idea might be viewed as contentious, why there should be any controversy around the idea of the wave function 'collapsing' is perhaps more subtle. Controversial it is though, because there is no mathematical description of it - just the observation that particles appear to obey the wave equation when you're not looking, and that they abruptly don't when you do. Sure, the Born Rule describes the probabilities associated with the outcomes of looking, but there is no actual description of the collapse itself. How does it happen? And why? Copenhagen is silent on these questions.

Further controversy lies in the act of 'observation' itself. There is an implied arbitrary line-in-the-sand that is drawn at an unspecified scale, where anything smaller exhibits this strange quantum-like behaviour, and anything larger instead obeys the everyday classical rules with which we are familiar. Copenhagen (at least in its original form) claims it to take a classical-scale system to perform the necessary 'observation', without which the quantum-scale target of the observation cannot switch modes from obeying the wave equation, to having physical reality.

There are clearly a number of fairly serious issues with this reading of events, and Einstein was aghast. As was Schrödinger.

How could the very building blocks of nature not have any form of physicality when nobody is looking? What exactly constitutes an observation? And how does a particle 'know' that it's being observed? How can you even observe something that is unphysical? Why do observations have to be made by macro-scale objects? And why should the outcomes of those observations be down to sheer chance? What is this arbitrary dividing line between the quantum and the classical anyway? Are all objects not made of quantum ingredients? Should they not display quantum behaviour too? If atoms don't really 'exist' as such when we're not looking, then shouldn't the same be true of the Moon?... And why should a macro-scale collection of atoms (such as a person) be able to collapse a wave function when the atoms it is made of cannot? Are we saying that reality is generated by consciousness?

Schrödinger came up with a famous thought experiment designed to illustrate what he saw as the absurdity of the interpretation. He imagined a cat trapped in a steel box with a vial of poison. The vial is sealed and waiting to be smashed by a hammer, which is activated by the click of a Geiger counter upon detection of radioactive decay from a small amount of material that is also in the box. The amount of radioactive material is small enough that the Geiger counter only has a fifty-fifty chance of detecting it.

So at some point, radioactive decay will occur and the Geiger counter will either detect it or not. If it does, then the vial will be smashed, the poison will be released, and the cat will die. Otherwise, the cat will live.

So according to the Copenhagen interpretation, he argued, as radioactive decay is a quantum event, and the fate of the cat is dependent upon it, then until someone opens the box and 'observes' what they find, the cat is neither dead nor alive, but is rather in some sort of strange superposition of dead and alive at the same time. If when you eventually do observe it, you find it to be dead, then it is you who killed it with your vicious act of looking!

The intention of Schrödinger's scathing dismissal of Copenhagen is unfortunately quite widely misunderstood, and is often held up as an example of the inherent strangeness of the quantum world, when it was actually intended as a fierce rebuttable to the very interpretation it is regularly used to popularise.

But in spite of the strong protestations of Einstein and Schrödinger - two of the founding fathers of the field - it quickly became the established orthodoxy, and to their dismay, became the default manner in which quantum theory was to be understood for (at least) the following twenty years.

By many, it is still understood in those terms today. Yet there is another interpretation that can be had, which changes nothing about the precision of Quantum Mechanic's predictive power, while offering a richer, more elegant understanding of the underlying reality. It has lead to practical outcomes which cannot be explained in terms of the Copenhagen understanding, and has astonishing consequences for the nature of time. We will turn to it shortly, but before we do, there is another strange feature of the quantum world that we must first explore. It too will be of critical importance to us. It is a feature known as 'entanglement'…

Between our brief glimpses,

Does the world not exist?

Is it summoned to being,

Through the touch of a thought?

In the darkest of corners,

Where the light rarely falls,

Doth reality waver,

And succumb to the night?

"Dear Schrödinger,

You are the only contemporary physicist, besides Laue, who sees that one cannot get around the assumption of reality - if only one is honest. Most of them simply do not see what sort of risky game they are playing with reality - reality as something independent of what is experimentally established."[9]

Albert Einstein

Across the void,

I feel you.

In the darkened silence,

I respond to your call...

Entanglement

Of the many strange features of Quantum Mechanics, there was one in particular that stood out as bothering Einstein the most - and ironically, it was one for whose discovery he was jointly responsible.

In 1935, he and his colleagues Boris Podolsky and Nathan Rosen, jointly published a paper outlining an effect that Schrödinger was to later call 'entanglement'. Their perspective was that the strange conclusions to which their paper led, should be taken as evidence that the quantum theory as it stood at the time, was incomplete - a view reflected in their provocative use of the title, 'Can Quantum-Mechanical Description of Physical Reality be Considered Complete?'.

They used the paper to argue that Quantum Mechanics must be an approximation of an as yet undiscovered deeper theory - one in which the effect they had uncovered must have a more readily acceptable explanation.

What they had discovered in the math, was the prediction of a bizarre physical phenomenon that occurs when either pairs or groups of particles are generated, interact, or share proximity. For these scenarios, it turns out that Quantum Mechanics predicts the adoption of a shared physical state, whereby the individual constituents cannot be described independently of each other.

The particles achieve this miraculous feat by virtue of the fact that an interaction between them causes them to share quantum information (become 'entangled'), which in turn means they are described by a single wave function as though they have become different aspects of a single object - like two sides of the same coin.

Figure 2.14

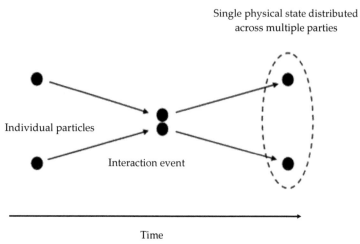

Single physical state distributed across multiple parties

Individual particles

Interaction event

Time

Before their interaction, each particle is described by its own wave function, and they can justifiably be thought of as separate objects. Post-interaction, they jointly share a single wave function, and their individuality becomes a murky concept which almost loses any meaning.

The main thrust of the argument that Einstein and his colleagues presented, was that in light of this entanglement, if you accept the Copenhagen interpretation and abandon the principle of realism (the idea that the world exists independently of what is measured, and that particles already have definitive properties before anyone looks), then it follows that you also have to abandon the principle of locality (the idea that no signals can propagate at speeds greater than the speed of light). This is because 'collapsing' a single wave function that is describing two particles (by making a measurement upon either of them), causes **both** to instantly manifest complementary values for the variable you have measured, regardless of any amount of spatial separation between them.

An entangled pair could be separated by the entire width of the universe, and the effect would still be instantaneous - measuring the value of some property for one, instantly fixes the value for the same property of the other, and that is a clear violation of the principle of locality - one of the most basic tenets of physics, and amongst the most sacrosanct of foundations of Special Relativity.

It is the rule which states that an object may only be directly influenced by its immediate surroundings. I.e. for an action or event at one location to exert an influence over something located elsewhere, then something (such as a wave in a field, or a particle) must carry that influence between them through space. When the Sun emits heat, for example, we are not instantly warmed here on Earth - the heat has to be transported to us in the form of photons, which arrive on the Earth approximately eight minutes after they leave the Sun. Or when the wind blows in London, the knock-on effects of that are not immediately felt in Paris - *if* the effects are ever to reach Paris, then they have to be transmitted through all the molecules of air that lie in between.

Through Special Relativity, these 'carriers' of effect - be they wave or particle - are limited in the speed at which they can travel, with none being able to exceed the speed of light. Everything in the universe is subject to this restriction, and yet if the Copenhagen interpretation is correct, it suggests that when it comes to the case of entangled particles, the ordinary rules of reality are somehow just simply discarded, with actions at one location causing instantaneous effects at far-flung places, in a manner that is completely indifferent to any concept of distance between them.

Consider the example of Bob and Alice examining an entangled pair of particles - let's say that one is an electron and the other is a positron, and that we give the electron to Bob, on Mars, and the positron to Alice, on Venus. Let's say that we are interested in their 'spin' property. Because they are entangled, we know that when we measure them, they will adopt opposing spins.

I've mentioned previously that spin is a strange property, so let me take a moment to explain. The 'spin' of a particle is a kind of intrinsic angular momentum it possesses, and is usually visualized as rotation around a given axis. When it is 'rotating' clockwise we think of the 'direction' of the axis as being 'up', and when it's 'rotating' anti-clockwise, we think of the 'direction' of the axis as being 'down'.

Figure 2.15

When we measure the spin, we refer to this 'direction' of the axis. However, these are particles and this is Quantum Mechanics, so obviously things are going to be a little stranger than that… Particles exist in a superposition of all spins, so the choice of axis is arbitrary. You can actually choose to measure the spin along any axis through the particle that you like, and whichever one you choose, you will find it 'spinning' upon it.

Figure 2.16

Now, recall from Heisenberg's uncertainty principle that the act of measuring a particle changes it. If Bob chooses an axis upon which to take the measurement of his particle, the particle adopts that axis over any of its others. Let's say that he chooses the vertical axis, and that when he does so, the wave function collapses and he finds it to be oriented 'up'. Since it was the same wave function that described Alice's particle, then hers must instantly adopt the same axis of spin too, and she must find it to be 'down'. The outcomes of their measurements are said to be 'correlated', and the instant nature of that correlation is uncaring of the distance that separates them - be it the distance between Venus and Mars, or the distance that separates opposite sides of the universe.

The issue presented by Einstein, Podolsky, and Rosen (EPR) was that in order to explain this, you had to do one of two things:

1) Accept the Copenhagen interpretation (abandon realism), and in doing so, also abandon the principle of locality. I.e. Accept that there must be some sort of communication between entangled parties that is faster than the speed of light - something along the lines of 'I have taken value x on axis z, therefore you must take value y on axis z'. This apparent faster-than-light communication was something which Einstein famously dubbed 'spooky action at a distance'.

2) Reject the Copenhagen interpretation, and in doing so retain the principles of realism and locality, but accept that the understanding of Quantum Mechanics is incomplete.

The EPR trio weighed-in on the side of option 2, postulating that particles do in fact posses definitive values for their properties before they are measured, and that it must only *appear* as though they are set by observation and the associated wave function collapse, because we don't have a full understanding of what's really going on.

Their perspective was that the violation of the speed of light which is necessary if you are to adopt Copenhagen, is clear evidence that it is wrong. There must instead exist, they claimed, some new and more fundamental theory which underlies Quantum Mechanics, which when known and understood, would transform the world of the quantum from one that is inherently probabilistic in nature (where the values of the properties of particles are randomly selected from a cloud of probabilities upon observation), into one which is deterministic (where the properties are predictable). This would thereby remove the incongruence of entanglements' spooky action, because without probabilities there is no need for wave function collapse, which means there is no need for any faster-than-light communication (because the properties of particles would be set from the outset). Einstein held this belief very dearly - a position summed up by his famous pronouncement that 'God does not play dice!'.

It had been EPR's expectation that others would agree with their assessment that the speed of light was simply too sacred to be sacrificed, but Bohr did not, and the debate that ensued was captured in a series of letters exchanged between Einstein and he, as they adopted opposing positions.

It's probably important to be clear that entanglement itself was not the thing that was in dispute - it was the nature of what it must imply. For Einstein it meant that Bohr's theory was incomplete, and for Bohr it meant the speed of light was not quite so mighty as Einstein would have had us believe. Both men, clearly had a lot at stake.

Much to Einstein's dismay, it was his treasured locality that was discarded by the mainstream opinion. The very tool intended to overthrow the orthodoxy of Copenhagen, had instead only served to strengthen it, as theorists found it more difficult to let go of the notion of wave-function collapse, than they did realism and locality.

Almost thirty years later, in 1964, the dichotomy between the positions was formalized by Sir John Bell, who demonstrated mathematically that (assuming realism is violated in the way that the Copenhagen interpretation suggests) no theory which sought to preserve the principal of locality could make the same predictions as those of Quantum Mechanics. This took the form of the now famous 'Bell Inequality', which places an upper limit on the levels of statistical correlation that can exist between entangled pairs in such a local theory.

In other words, if the correlations of measurements predicted by entanglement are facilitated via some form of as-yet unknown deeper theory which preserves the principle of locality, then there is a statistical limit to how often the measured correlations could just happen through sheer chance.

Crucially, this limit is lower than the levels predicted by Quantum Mechanics, and as such provides a means by which the issue can be probed experimentally - if the levels of correlation observed through experiment violate the Bell Inequality (I.e. are higher than the statistical limit of what they could reach through luck), then an underlying localistic theory is ruled out. Conversely, if the inequality is not violated, then locality is supported, and some form of deeper theory must be underlying the world of the quantum, awaiting our discovery. Such postulated deeper theories are called 'hidden variable' theories, as they assume there is some 'hidden' information we are currently unaware of, which once known, will reveal Quantum Mechanics to be deterministic.

Bell's great insight shifted the parameters of the debate, moving it from the realm of philosophy and personal taste, into the arena of things which can be explored empirically through experiment.

Such experimental tests duly followed, and the results were not considered good news for the position adopted by EPR. They demonstrate invariably that when particles are in an entangled state, the outcomes of measurements performed upon them do indeed display correlations that exceed Bell's statistical limit.

Over the years, more and more experiments have been performed, pushing the limits of credulity with the lengths to which they have gone in order to verify and re-verify the results. The particles have been separated over greater and greater distances before the measurements are taken - in order to confirm definitively they have influenced each other faster than the speed of light; Random number generators have been used to pick the axes of measurement - just in case the experimenters are unwittingly under some kind of unknown influence when they choose them; The random polarization of light from ultra-distant galaxies has even been used to choose the axes, just in case our random number generators are under some such unknown influence!

Whatever lengths have been gone to in any of these experiments, the outcome has always been the same - every single time. The Bell Inequalities are always violated by the correlations of measurement outcomes, when those measurements are performed on entangled pairs.

The result is clear. The Bell tests rule out locality if it's the act of observation that gives particles their properties, and there can be no alternative theory in which that is not the case.

So while Einstein was correct that to account for entanglement in Bohr's interpretation, you have to be willing to accept communication at speeds greater than the speed of light, he was wrong about there being an underlying hidden variable theory that would show Quantum Mechanics to be deterministic (assuming it's observation that sets the properties of the particles).

For many, dropping realism and locality is a lot to swallow, and while the more fundamental theory Einstein had hoped would emerge is indeed ruled out by experimental results, that is not to say that Bohr's interpretation was correct.

The restriction of the speed of light need only be violated if Quantum Mechanics is indeed inherently probabilistic, but what if it is not? Such a suggestion, certainly in Einstein's day, was tantamount to heresy, but what if there really was a different perspective that could be found? What if there could be a different understanding of the quantum theory itself?

There is in fact a particular peculiarity of entanglement which seems to hint at this. It is that although a causal influence appears to be somehow able to break the speed of light, information about it having done so does not. Bob and Alice only get to find out about the influence their particles have had on each other when they message each other to announce their results, and those messages are restricted to travel at the speed of light. This is something called the 'No-Signalling Theorem' - the rule that entanglement cannot be used to send a message. So we have a situation whereby causality can propagate faster than light, but information about it having done so cannot, and that smells suspicious.

Could this be a signpost that something isn't quite right? Could there be an alternative way of looking at Quantum Mechanics that doesn't harbour such intractable difficulties?…

As it turns out, there is, and we shall examine this possibility closely in the next chapter. Unfortunately for Einstein, it was not posited until a year after his death, and he sadly took his frustration at the situation with him to the grave.

But while the mechanism by which entanglement really works is controversial (even to this day), what isn't subject to any level of debate is the fact that the phenomenon is very real. Following an interaction of any kind, the individual constituents of that interaction can no longer be viewed as independent entities, but should instead be considered as parts of a single inseparable whole. There is a shared physical state that is distributed across them, and no individual piece of the whole can be properly described without consideration of the others.

This shared state can be exploited, and is used today as the basis of 'quantum cryptography', which is the technology that underpins the most modern of secure communications.

The entanglement; the 'one-ness' of the system, persists in its fullness until the next interaction upon that system occurs, at which point some of the quantum information is transferred into a new entanglement (with the new interacting party), and is irreversibly lost with regards to the original system. When this happens, we say that the original system has 'decohered', by which we mean that it has lost some of its quantum information to its environment.

Entanglement, decoherence, and the associated shared physical states, are going to prove to be of critical interest as we explore potential mechanisms behind our mysterious flow of time. As we shall also see shortly, they are likewise a key element in unlocking the mysteries of the quantum, providing an incredible insight into the true, and dazzling structure of the world.

*"Entanglement is not **one**,*
*but rather **the** characteristic trait of quantum mechanics."*[10]

Erwin Schrödinger

Though two,

We are one.

No distance may part us,

Nor time dull our bond,

Your touch is as mine,

My experience yours,

I'm the heads to your tails,

And to your action defer.

Through shadow lands,
Where once concealed,
Astounding truth,
Shall be revealed...

The Infinite Tree

As a reaction to the inherent outlandishness of quantum mechanics, many theorists stopped questioning meaning, and retreated instead to the relative comfort of instrumentalism. This is essentially the view that it doesn't matter what it all means, just so long as the math works and is useful. It is characterised by the edict of 'shut up and calculate'.

Quantum mechanics, being our most exquisitely precise and successful theory of all time, is exceptionally useful, and it is true that one can put it to good practical use without having to bother with troublesome questions such as how it is representative of reality, or what it might imply from a philosophical point of view.

Some estimates put the contribution that quantum-based technology makes to the GDP of some western nations, as high as 25%. Everything from transistors and LED's, to TV's, digital cameras, solar cells, computers, lasers, GPS systems, etc. are reliant upon it. It has played a critical role in the development of materials with specific optical, electrical, and magnetic properties, and is by all accounts a critical component of our modern world. It may actually be easier, in fact, to ask what modern technologies are *not* reliant upon it.

Very few of the people involved in the design and manufacture of such things though, realise it is quantum mechanics which is being utilised at the heart of what they do. Fewer still have any sort of understanding of it, and even fewer care for its meaning. Scientific discovery can manifest many useful practical applications without any requirement for explanation. But this is to miss the very essence of science, and while for the vast majority of us this is OK, for scientists it should not be enough.

Science does not exist simply to provide useful technology, or tools (instruments) for calculation and prediction. It is not the vacuous cranking-out of numbers in order to do helpful things. It is the quest for knowledge; for understanding. To accept it being shorn of its explanatory power, is to abandon our curiosity and resign ourselves to a functionalism that is devoid of the human spirit of adventure.

That is not to say there is no merit in discovery if we do not seek its meaning, but is to suggest that its contribution of value to our body of knowledge is significantly diminished.

In the face of such intractably mind-boggling questions as those presented by the realm of the quantum though, it is difficult to criticise those who adopt an instrumentalist approach for doing so.

The fact is that science occasionally comes to an impasse, where the problems are of such monumental difficulty that further progression is dependent upon the advent of a genius. But every now and then, such people come along. One such man was a graduate student of John Wheeler - a man by the name of Hugh Everett.

In 1956, he submitted for his PhD thesis one of the most beautifully crafted and audaciously spectacular physics papers ever written. At its heart lay the basic sentiment that as quantum mechanics is the most successful theory of all time, then what happens if we take it seriously as a description of nature? What happens if we interpret it literally, and follow it through to its logical conclusion? The wave function describes the evolution of matter and energy over time. As everything is made of these ingredients, then what happens if we stop pretending (as we rightly ought to) that the observer and measuring apparatus are not a part of the quantum world too? What happens if we apply the theory to the universe as a whole?

The answers to these questions, would turn out to be stunning.

Not only would they do away with problematic issues such as observer-dependent reality, wave function collapse, indeterminate futures, and spooky action at a distance, but would present a picture of reality so shockingly incongruous, that it would be decades before it was taken seriously by the mainstream of physics.

Today it is known as the 'Many Worlds' interpretation of Quantum Mechanics, and is very much a mainstream view. To call it an 'interpretation' though is to do it an injustice, for it is not really an interpretation at all - it is the bare theory laid out in its pure form. Everett did not falsely add anything to it (such as a notion like wave function collapse, for example). In fact he didn't add anything at all - he simply applied quantum mechanics as it stood to the universe as a whole, and accurately recognised what the math had been saying all along. The great genius of his idea, was in its simplicity.

At its heart, were three great realisations.

The first was that the universe in its entirety is quantum mechanical. Quantum theory is ordinarily applied to isolated micro-scale systems, but it makes no sense to treat systems other than the whole universe as being completely isolated from their environments, because in nature that simply isn't the case, and is exceedingly difficult to achieve for any period of time in the lab.

Light inside a box, for example, interacts with the atoms from which the box is made, so the box must be considered part of the system. The atoms of the box in turn interact with each other, and with the air molecules on the outside. Those air molecules interact with the room, which interacts with the environment, which is struck by sunlight, which interacts with the cosmic microwave background... etc.

It doesn't take much reasoning to arrive at the conclusion that when studying a photon, or an atom, what you are really looking at is just a small part of a wider quantum system. The wave function of the photon you are examining, exists as a sub-system of a wider whole, and that wider whole has a wave function too.

The second great realisation was simply that by extension of the first, any measuring apparatus or observers are themselves contained within the wave function of that wider whole, and as such cannot be considered as 'external' elements. The only way they could be rightly treated as external, is if they were somehow outside of Spacetime itself - which they are not. They are by definition, a part of the universe.

A 'universe' is defined by its content. In fact, it **is** its content. There is no 'container' as such - it is rather the collective of energy, matter, and events that happen therein. In the same way that each moment in the Everywhen (each Now Slice) is defined by its matter and energy content, so too is a universe.

The observer then, forms an inherent part of the system, and must be accounted for within it. They are a sub-system of the wider whole, and the arbitrary conceptual division between micro-scale and macro-scale systems simply isn't there.

So if the whole universe is a quantum system, and there can be no observers external to it, then it follows that there can be no externally-induced wave function 'collapse'. There is nothing external to do it! Any such collapse (or the impression of one) must be triggered from within.

The third realisation was to understand that any interaction between two internal sub-systems constitutes a measurement (an observation) upon both. When a photon collides with an atom for example, they in effect 'measure' each other. Consciousness and human knowledge do not come into the picture.

There is of course, another thing we know of that happens every time there is an interaction - it's called 'entanglement'. All measurement and observation processes should actually be regarded as interactions between observer and object-systems, which produce strong correlations. Measurement, is in fact an entanglement phenomenon which occurs between relative sub-systems.

From these three 'obvious' facts, incredible insights into the structure of reality were to be gained. Let us begin by considering a single electron being put through its paces in a classic double slit experiment.

We perceive it as passing through both slits as a wave, before 'becoming' a particle when it impacts upon the detection screen at one of the possible locations dictated by Schrödinger's wave equation.

Before its impact, at each time-step it is in a superposition of all the possible positions it could take. This is Heisenberg's uncertainty principle in action. That is to say, there are many potential 'paths' or 'histories' the electron might have.

There is actually nothing in the math which makes any one of those histories any more valid than the rest, and Everett discarded our natural and unjustified bias for assuming singularity, and instead trusted what the equations were saying - he chose to treat all histories in the superposition on an equal basis... as all having equal reality.

From that marvellous leap, miraculous things were to follow.

What he had seen, was that if all elements of the superposition have equal reality, then the so-called paradox of Schrödinger's superposition of dead and alive cats, wasn't describing a single cat that was in some sort of weird simultaneously dead-alive state - it was describing multiplicity. It was describing two cats...

In the case of our electron, the superposition doesn't describe one electron that is in many potential places - it describes many instances of that one electron, each in their own very distinct place, but in different histories.

The wave we perceive is actually that myriad of instances, all interfering with each other, and the wave function describes their behaviour as a collective. But if they are in different histories, then how can they interfere? At this point, it is probably prudent to say a word about a strange feature of particles, known as 'fungibility'.

If two things are 'fungible', it means they are not only identical, but readily interchangeable too.

Numbers are an example of this - If you begin with an initial 2, and then you add 2 to it, then you have 4. If you then subtract 2, then you have 2 again. But is that 2 you end up with the same 2 that you started with? Or is it the 2 that you added? Perhaps it is made up of one half of the original 2, and one half of what you added? The point is, it makes no difference, and it makes no sense to ask. The numbers are fungible.

If we combine the concepts of numbers and children though, then the fungibility of the numbers is broken - if I drop 2 children off at day-care, then I sure as hell care whether or not it's the same 2 children I receive back at the end of the day, and it sure as hell makes a difference!

At the macro-scale level of the classical world we inhabit, it is largely conceptual things which are fungible (think barrels of oil, electronic money, etc). In the micro-scale world of the quantum though, counter-intuitively, electrons, photons, and most atoms are fungible too.

Particles will readily exchange properties with one another, and if you put two of them in a box, for example, it makes little sense to ask which of them is which when you take them out.

Returning to our double slit experiment, although they are in different histories, the many instances of our electron existing within the superposition are at this point, all fungible. Their fungibility is mediated by the fact that the wave function describing them is what we call 'coherent', by which we mean that all of its components (each electron instance in the superposition) are vibrating in almost exact synchronisation. Because of this, they are able to interact, and do so by interfering with each other - adding and subtracting depending upon their phase - to produce the 'wave' which we perceive. This is how the 'single' electron manages to pass through both slits at once - it's because it is really many instances of itself in fungible and overlapping parallel histories, which interfere...

The trans-history wave of electrons propagates through space until a measurement is made - In this case, until it strikes the detection screen in our experiment. And at this point, something wonderful happens...

Let us focus in on just one of the instances of the electron - on a single eigenstate of the superposition.

At the moment of 'measurement', that instance entangles with the atom that it strikes in the screen. When this happens, it acquires entanglement information which differentiates it from all of the other instances of itself, thereby breaking the fungibility it had with them. This decouples it from the rest of wave function - preventing it from having any further interactions with the other components, and we say that it has 'decohered'.

It has, in effect, become 'cut off' from the other elements in the superposition. Those other elements are all still there, and continue evolving in accordance with the Schrödinger equation - they can just no longer have any interaction with our particular instance, which is now evolving independently from them.

Meanwhile, as has been mentioned, the atom in the detection screen is entangled with that instance - with a single history in the original electron wave. That atom too had its own superposition, of course, and it's just one element of it that is entangled with the electron. That instance of the atom decoheres from the atom superposition too, just like the electron instance did from its own. They have 'measured' each other.

The two instances have formed a composite system, and can no longer be described independently from each other. From this point on, they evolve together in accordance with their own wave function, which is an independent sub-system of both original atom and electron waves.

Figure 2.17

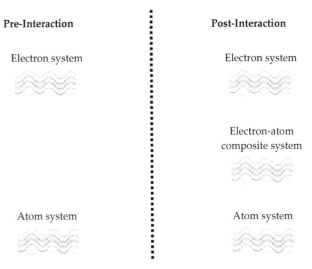

Pre-Interaction	Post-Interaction
Electron system	Electron system
	Electron-atom composite system
Atom system	Atom system

The atom then interacts with its neighbours, and in doing so entangles them too, repeating the same process of decoherence. Those then interact with their neighbours, and so on. Very quickly (at the speed of light), the entire detection screen is affected, and the decohering effects of the original entanglement of the electron and the atom it struck, are amplified up to the macro-scale level.

Let us then suppose that one of the atoms in the decohered screen is soon struck by a photon of light, which becomes entangled with it and 'rebounds' off (through absorption and re-emission). The photon is decohered from its own superposition in the same manner, and is shortly afterwards detected by the observers' eye. Then by the same process, the observer themself entangles and decoheres too.

And here's the real magic - because of the way they are entangled, our observer is no longer able to perceive the other instances of the electron in the original wave (because the one to whose history they are bound is no longer fungible with the rest), and from their perspective, the wave function instantaneously 'collapses' into that single eigenstate - an event which they witness as the miraculous metamorphosis from electron wave to electron particle.

In other words, the observer's perception of wave function collapse is an illusion based upon their entanglement. There is in fact no such thing as 'collapse'. The other instances of the electron are actually all still there - our measuring equipment and observer just simply can't interact with them in any way (including perceiving them), because their histories have become decoherent.

With the appearance of wave function collapse revealed to be a mere trick of the light - no more than an elaborately conjured illusion of perspective, there is a spell-binding consequence for the true structure of the world...

This is born of the fact that the other elements of the superposition are not destroyed, but continue in their own evolution. Let's take a look at what that means.

So far, we have considered only the chain of events that happen involving one individual history of the electron (one eigenstate of its superposition), but with all eigenstates having equal validity, the others interact with the detection screen too!

What I have just described happening for that one instance of the electron, in fact happens individually to them **all**. Each one of them (and there are typically trillions) also entangle with the screen, decohere from their superposition, and bind the screen to each of their own histories. So we have a situation whereby the measuring apparatus is 'branched' into many different timelines.

Figure 2.18

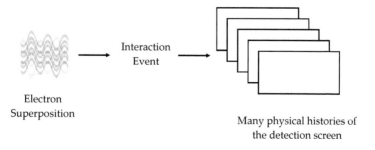

Electron
Superposition

Many physical histories of
the detection screen

Those timelines are differentiated by the exact position of the electron instance by which they were struck.

Each history then progresses as normal, with a photon striking the screen in each of them, and rebounding into the observer's eye, entangling them. So we end up with a situation whereby the observer (being also composed of quantum ingredients), is themselves branched into many (trillions) different versions.

Through the process of decoherence, those versions are very quickly completely isolated from one another. The lightning-quick speed at which that isolation happens means they are unable to become aware of each other (because they find themselves in different non-fungible histories).

Figure 2.19

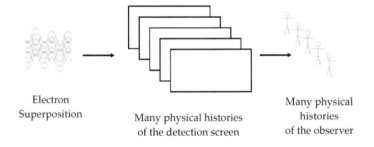

Electron
Superposition

Many physical histories
of the detection screen

Many physical
histories
of the observer

At this point, the many instances of the observer have to all intents and purposes, become 'trapped' in non-interacting parallel worlds.

They all share a common branching point, before which they all perceived the electron as a wave. They all believe they are the only version of themselves; they all have the impression they are in the only timeline that exists; and they all perceive the electron wave as having collapsed into a single particle. The only difference between them, is precisely where they find the particle located, and each branched observer has the impression that the location of 'their' particle was randomly selected from the superposition of potentials (in accordance with the application of the Born rule to the probability amplitudes).

When we talk of a parallel 'world', we mean an almost autonomous history of the universe ('almost' because of the interference effects that fungible histories can bring to bear upon each other, before entanglement happens). There is a constantly branching web of such parallel histories, which collectively we term the 'Multiverse', and to which I refer to in the title of this chapter as 'The Infinite Tree'.

Immediately following each branching point in the multiverse, the ensuing histories are almost identical to each other, but with each passing measurement event, they become more and more differentiated.

Figure 2.20

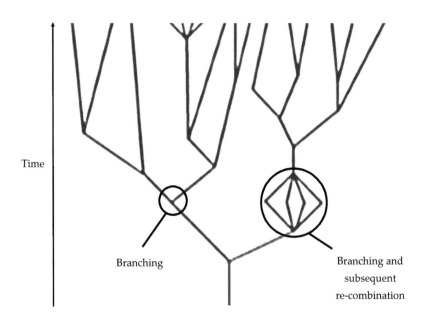

Time

Branching

Branching and
subsequent
re-combination

Occasionally, and if it happens quickly enough (before further measurements cause greater differentiation through further splitting), then histories can recombine. An example of this is highlighted in figure 2.20. This is what we witness as interference in the double slit experiment. It is the recombination of histories that have branched but not become differentiated.

The same effect can be shown very nicely in the classic 'paradox' of the Mach-Zehnder interferometer:

Figure 2.21

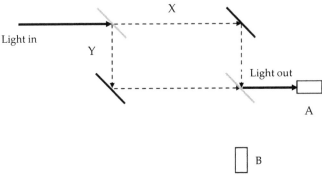

The set-up is quite straight forwards - The grey bars are semi-silvered mirrors that have a 50% chance of letting photons pass through them, and a 50% chance of reflecting them instead. The black bars are standard mirrors which reflect photons 100% of the time, and are there only to steer them toward the 2nd semi-silvered mirror. The two detectors, A and B, register where light is detected emerging from the apparatus.

When light is shone into the experiment, some of it ends up travelling along path X, and some of it along path Y. The two paths re-join at the 2nd semi-silvered mirror, and the interference that creates means that you only find light coming into detector A. This is probably pretty much what you might expect. The thing that is perhaps more surprising is that the same result is obtained when you fire single photons into it one at a time.

Faced with different potential outcomes with regards which path is taken at the semi-silvered mirrors, each photon enters a superposition and takes both of them at the same time. I.e. reality is split into two parallel 'worlds' (histories). In one history, the photon goes one way, and in the other it goes the other. Those histories recombine at the 2nd semi-silvered mirror, producing the interference that results in the photon being found at detector A 100% of the time.

This would not be possible if there were really only one instance of the photon in the apparatus... In that case, you would expect to find it at detector A 50% of the time, and the other 50% at detector B. The outcome we actually get is made possible by the fact that history splits in two before recombining, and demonstrates very nicely that all elements of the superposition should be regarded on an equal basis - as all having equally legitimate physicality. Particles are irreducibly multiversal objects, and their fungible parallel histories overlap and interfere.

The very phenomenon of interference then, is the recombination of weakly differentiated histories, and we are back at an understanding of how the electron 'wave' that we began with, actually occurs.

Returning to the double slit experiment once again, we can now also see why it is that we get the strange outcome that a measurement taken ahead of the slits, changes the experimental result that we perceive. Here's a quick reminder of the setup:

Figure 2.22

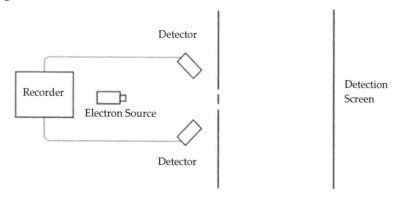

Recall that observing the electrons to see which slit they are passing through alters the pattern we find at the detection screen from one of interference, to a pattern of two bright bands that are consistent with the idea of electrons as particles, rather than electrons as waves.

Figure 2.23

What is really happening here is that the fungibility of the electron instance that is observed ahead of the slits, is broken by that act of observation (measurement). It becomes entangled with one of the detectors, and in doing so, decoheres from the rest of the wave. Having undergone that decoherence, it cannot interact with its counterparts in other histories, and so passes through the slits unaffected by the interference that would otherwise imbue it with its characteristic wave-like behaviour.

As observers who have entangled with that particular history, we are left with the impression that the electron somehow 'knew' that it was being observed, and mischievously adjusted its behaviour accordingly - like a child who begins whistling innocently once it becomes apparent that their parents are watching them misbehave.

In reality the electron does not actually 'know' anything, of course - it is simply that we have decohered it earlier in the experiment, and the results that we see are a direct consequence of that fact. It suddenly adopts the behaviour of a particle rather than wave because through our observation of it, we have suddenly separated it from its wave. We have bound ourselves to specific eigenstates of its superposition, and in doing so have been branched into many parallel timelines, in each of which we find it to be in an ever-so-slightly different (but definitive) state.

As a point of clarity, there is just one underlying fundamental reality (one universe, if you will), and it consists of superpositions of state which through processes of self-measurement, give rise to an emergent multiverse of parallel quasi-classical histories, which for all intents and purposes may (because following decoherence they will not interact) be thought of as parallel worlds.

But what does this plethora of parallel timelines, constantly splitting and recombining mean for our picture of dynamics in the Everywhen? What does it mean for the flow of time?

So far, nothing.

Although the 'universe' branches at every decision point, the branches are not really 'created' at the point of measurement, of course - as with everything else on the stage of the Everywhen, they are all pre-existing, and there are still no objective dynamics.

The future, and by that I mean **all** of it in its mind-bogglingly many branched versions, is still already there. The theory of the universal wave function (AKA 'Quantum Mechanics') introduces plurality to the Everywhen - not subjective dynamics. It means there are many static timelines, instead of the single one presumed by Einstein and Minkowski. Time it would seem, is not only deep, but broad...

All futures that could possibly occur, actually do. We shall return to this in a subsequent chapter, when we look again at the issue of choice, and what that means in a world where every possible outcome of a quantum event actually happens.

One thing we can say at this point though, is that the abandonment of a single-history world-view successfully returns determinism to the equation. The multiverse is by its very nature, entirely deterministic. 'Random' events only appear random from the perspective of an observer (their awareness being confined to a single history).

Consider for example, the so-called random event of the detection/non-detection of radioactive decay in the case of Schrödinger's cat. Globally across the multiverse, there is nothing at all that is random about the outcome here - both detection and non-detection happen (on different branches), and that fact is entirely predictable. It is only from the limited vantage point of one of the resulting histories (where our observer finds either one result or the other) that the illusion is created that just one outcome occurred, and that which one it was, was the result of a random process.

Figure 2.24

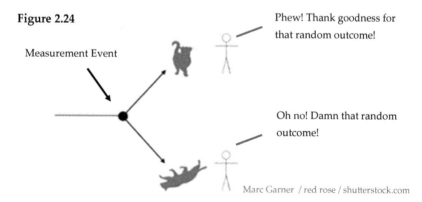

Measurement Event

Phew! Thank goodness for that random outcome!

Oh no! Damn that random outcome!

Marc Garner / red rose / shutterstock.com

126

In fact, the only thing that can be argued to be probabilistic, is the answer to the question of which branch any particular instance of the observer finds themselves on afterwards. There are copies of the observer in all of them, but each instance experiences only one. Which one is it? - This is a question we call 'self-locating uncertainty' - although all outcomes happen, immediately after the instant of measurement any particular observer is ignorant of which of the branches they are on. The probabilities associated with the answers to this question, are the ones that are given by the Born rule.

The observer of course discovers the answer when he looks at the outcome of the measurement.

The Born rule, it turns out, does not give the probabilities of which eventuality will emerge from the superposition (because they all do), but instead gives the relative 'weightings' of each branch that is realised, where the weights correspond to the chances of you being the observer experiencing any particular branch post-measurement.

Another example of deterministic events having the *appearance* of randomness from within a single history, is that of the supposed randomness of the position on the screen at which a particle will turn out to be located in a double-slit experiment. As all outcomes happen, globally the process is not random, but entirely deterministic.

This global determinism across all histories that turns out to have been hiding in the quantum theory all along, is of great consequence. Without it, we are left with a single-history world view in which, as discussed in the previous chapter, we are forced to invoke some kind of mysterious 'spooky action at a distance' in order to explain the measurement outcomes of entanglement.

In a multiversal view, the explanation behind the great mystery falls neatly into place quite naturally, because the inherent randomness which lay at the heart of the issue, isn't really there. Because there is no wave function collapse, there is no need for any instantaneous communication because measurement outcomes occur deterministically and globally across branches. Those branches propagate at the speed of light, carrying a causal influence with them as they go, and thereby preserving the principle of locality.

To see how this works, consider the example of Bob and Alice performing a typical Bell test experiment, where the outcomes of their measurement events are shared with their friend, Charlie. Let's suppose they are measuring the spin of two entangled particles along axes that are offset by 45°, and that all three friends are spatially separated.

In this scenario, classical mechanics predicts that they will find complementary opposing values for the direction of the spin axis approximately 75% of the time, whereas Quantum Mechanics gives a forecast of about 85% (the prediction is not for a 100% correlation because we are deliberately measuring the particles using different axes, offset from each other by 45° - a 100% correlation would be predicted by Quantum Mechanics in the case where they were measured along the same axis).

Figure 2.25

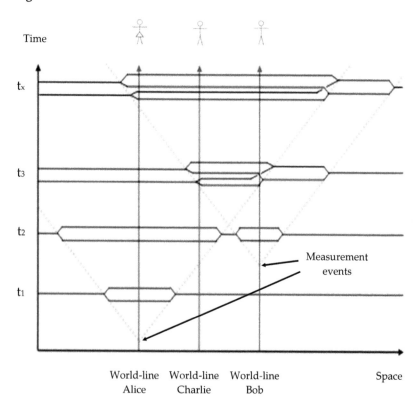

The dashed lines indicate the paths taken by rays of light that could theoretically emanate from the measurement events. These are the boundaries of the causal influences as they propagate through space and time. They can be thought of as the 'wave-fronts' of the branching processes originating from each measurement. The horizontal lines represent branching.

From figure 2.25, we can see that Alice takes her measurement first. If we were to take a snapshot of the multiverse at time t_1 we would find that as a result of her actions, she had been branched. She exists at that time in two different histories - one in which she measured spin 'up', and one in which she measured spin 'down'. The causal influence of that measurement has not yet had the opportunity to reach either Charlie or Bob though - it is carried towards them at the speed of light by the branching process, which has not yet propagated that far through the spacetime. So Bob and Charlie exist only on the single branch that was present before Alice's measurement was made, and that measurement has not yet done anything at all to the state of Bob's particle.

At time t_2 the branching initiated by Alice has reached Charlie, and branched him too. He too now exists in a timeline where Alice measured 'up', and a timeline where she measured 'down' (and enough time has passed that in each of those branches, he could have received a signal from Alice indicating the result). Meanwhile, Bob has made the measurement of his particle, and is similarly branched into two additional timelines. The instances of Bob in those histories each know the value for their own measurement - one of them is 'up', and the other is 'down'. His branching though, has not yet reached either Charlie or Alice.

At time t_3 we can see that the causal influences of both Alice and Bob's measurements have reached Charlie, and that as a result he is branched into four histories (as is Bob). Those histories represent the four different combinations of outcomes of the two measurements. They are where the measurements were up-up, up-down, down-up, and down-down.

Alice too, will soon find herself in this situation (see t_x on figure 2.25), as the area of intersection of the causal influences of those two measurements grows forwards in time, and engulfs her. It is this region of Spacetime (where the future light cones of the two measurement events intersect), that gives rise to the kind of statistical results that present us with a violation of the Bell Inequality.

Figure 2.26

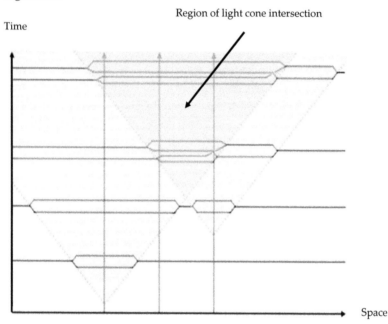

In this region, the weightings of the four branches are not equal, but are set by the weightings of the branching initiated by Alice and Bob propagating outwards via the light cones. The branches where the particles have opposing values end up accounting for 85% of the weighting, and the ones where they don't, account for just 15%.

If the three friends repeat this experiment enough times, they note that 85% of the time they find a violation of the Bell Inequality, and they go on to conclude that the predictions of Quantum Mechanics are correct. They also note that there was not enough time between the measurement events for a light-speed causal influence to have travelled between them. If they have not heard of the Many Worlds interpretation (or perhaps simply do not believe it to be accurate), they infer that there must have been some kind of instantaneous communication between the particles, whereas if they *do* know about it (and believe it to be true), they find nothing spooky about it at all, but instead draw the conclusion that the entirely deterministic branching process propagated the weightings forwards in a perfectly well-behaved manner that is in accordance with both locality and realism.

They further conclude that those who insist upon the necessity of instantaneous communication, do so because they begin from the erroneous position that there is only one physically realised history.

The 'Many Worlds' and the 'Copenhagen' interpretations can be thought of as being generally representative of two different categories of interpretation of quantum mechanics - namely those which postulate the existence of wave function 'collapse' in addition to the natural evolution of the system (as embodied by Copenhagen), and those which rely upon the system's natural evolution alone (as embodied by Many Worlds).

If we exclude hidden-variable theories (which are ruled-out by the Bell test results), then there are no collapse interpretations which retain either realism or locality. Meanwhile, there are no non-collapse interpretations which do not result in many physically realised versions of history. So if you don't accept that things have no physical existence outside of what is measured, you have no choice but to accept that they have that physical existence across a multitude of timelines. There is no option which denies both of these things. Barring the discovery of some as-yet undreamt of interpretation, you must choose your poison, so to speak - one or the other.

The difference between the two viewpoints, basically boils down to different opinions on the meaning of the quantum superposition. Collapse interpretations treat superpositions as non-physical, whereas non-collapse interpretations treat them as real. Both approaches yield the same predictions regarding the outcomes of experiment, but offer profoundly differing explanations of reality.

The interpretations that treat superpositions as physically real however, offer the simpler and more conservative explanation, as there is nothing 'falsely' added to them. The concept of collapse is deliberately added into the other interpretations by hand, precisely in order to avoid the plurality that the natural dynamics of the wave function leads to. It is falsely grafted-on in order to bring theory in line with observation, but as we have seen, macro-scale superpositions disappear from the perspective of the observer anyway (via the process of entanglement and decoherence), so their forced removal from the picture is not necessary.

If the application of Occam's razor (the fact that the simplest explanation is usually the best) is not enough to rule in favour of multiple histories, then (in my opinion) the price that collapse interpretations have to pay through needing to discard realism, ought to be.

Einstein may have been wrong about quantum theory being incomplete, yet the explanations he was hoping some hidden variable theory might provide, can instead be found residing inherently within Quantum Mechanics itself. There's no need to add either collapse or hidden variables into the picture - you just have to be prepared to accept what the math is saying... and inescapably, it is describing multiplicity...

It is saying there are many worlds.

"The quantum theory of parallel universes [...] is not some troublesome, optional interpretation emerging from arcane theoretical considerations. It is the explanation - the only one that is tenable - of a remarkable and counter-intuitive reality"[11]

David Deutsch

A shimmer of starlight on the face of creation,

The impenetrable depths of the wilderness true,

All souls in their place,

In the vast hall of nature,

With infinite faces,

Unknowing their paths,

- The endless seas on which we sail,

The countless suns that warm our backs,

The boundless scenes beneath the veil,

From plain sight hidden,

The kingdom whole.

Exploiting Plurality

It's not difficult to see why it took so long for the revelation of Many Worlds to become widely accepted. While the logic is easy enough to follow (and difficult to refute), and while it intrinsically makes sense of issues that had previously only been resolvable through the mystical incantation of faster-than-light communication, the prediction of physically real parallel histories is so outrageously alien to our experience and expectation, that it can be difficult to admit.

In that sense, perhaps one of the most difficult aspects of it is that it is not just the things of the micro-scale world to which it applies, but the things of the macro-scale world too - and most critically, us. So long as it's just fundamental particles of which we speak, the idea feels abstracted away from us enough that we can accept it on its merit, but once we realise that we ourselves are constructed of those fundamental particles and so must naturally be subject to the same branching process, it suddenly feels much more close to home. For some, perhaps too close for comfort.

Macro-scale objects interact with their environments almost instantly. For an object such as a person, for example, the chances of not having an interaction with another particle at any given instant are vanishingly small. Because of this, they are constantly re-entangling with their environment and decohering - branching is therefore a universal and near constant phenomenon.

In an early critique of Everett's ideas, the physicist Bryce DeWitt began an exchange of letters with him, in which he laid out a series of objections.

Everett answered them one by one, and in a last-ditch appeal to 'common sense', DeWitt observed that he simply didn't feel as though he split into multiple copies every time he interacted with another particle. Everett's response was short, and devastating -

"Do you feel the Earth move?", he asked - A reference to the Inquisition's rejection of Galileo's insight that the Earth orbits the sun, on the basis that they could not feel the motion.

With this, DeWitt conceded, and in fact went on to later become one of the Many Worlds interpretation's greatest proponents.

Since that time, it has risen to prominence partly due to its elegance and simplicity; partly because it has robustly stood the test of time; partly due to ongoing research into quantum gravity (which we shall look at in close detail in Part 3); and partly due to the progress that is being made in the field of quantum computing.

Those advancements in quantum computing are difficult to explain in terms other than those of Many Worlds, for quantum computers are not just fast and clever versions of ordinary everyday computers - they are an entirely different category of beast altogether, and have been designed specifically to exploit the parallelism that is inherent in all superpositions... the parallelism of time.

I ask the reader to suspend disbelief for a moment, and to imagine a world in which we were able to construct devices capable of isolating a number of particles from their environment, so as to prevent their superpositions from decohering through entanglement with their surroundings. They would do this in order that the particles with which they were concerned, could each be held in a superposition of multiple values with regards to a particular variable.

Let's further suppose that we could then make use of those superpositions, by putting them to work on some difficult (and therefore ordinarily time-consuming) calculation, by distributing elements of that calculation across their myriad superposed elements

Having taken measures to supress decoherence, each element in a superposition would remain fungible and able to interact with the others, and so we could perhaps make use of the process of interference (re-combination) between them, in order to obtain an overall result.

So we would in effect be distributing the calculation across parallel (but only weakly differentiated) timelines, before bringing them back together to form a single history in which we read-off the result.

That world in which such devices have been invented, is in fact *this* world, and they are called quantum computers.

The origins of the concept date back to 1959, when the possibility of making use of quantum effects for computation was first proposed by the distinguished physicist, Richard Feynman (another student of the great John Wheeler). His interest was primarily in how to build a computer capable of simulating the behaviour of quantum systems, and the conclusion that he came to (correctly) was that the only way to keep track of all the variables involved was to have an actual quantum system do it for you. So the idea was to have a quantum system that could simulate other quantum systems.

What Feynman managed to conceptualise was a machine which could be re-configured to simulate different target quantum systems, but we were some distance from ever being able to realise the concept at the time.

It wasn't until 1980 that the field was founded proper by Paul Benioff and Yuri Manin. IBM took an instant interest, and co-organised a conference with MIT, at which Feynman spoke and urged the world to go ahead and take up the challenge of actually building a quantum computer. It is a challenge that was seized upon with relish, and steady progress has since been made in terms of practical implementation, with devices constructed of more and more qubits being created and put to use.

A 'qubit' (quantum bit) is the quantum version of the classical 'bit' used in mainstream computer science. It can be in a quantum state of either 1, 0, or a superposition of both (in which it is simultaneously, 1, 0, both, and neither).

Preventing the superpositions from decohering has been one of the main challenges in the construction of machines with more and more qubits, with the difficulties of isolating them from the environment for long enough to perform the necessary calculations being an area of intense research and exploration.

At the time of writing, systems of up to seventy two qubits have been demonstrated using superconducting circuits.

Such machines are not suited to all types of calculation though - only ones which are amenable to the production of a result via the adding and subtracting of waves, but the factorisation of large numbers is an example of a calculation that falls into that category.

Factorising numbers, particularly large ones, is a problem that is very hard for classical computers to solve.

Consider the following multiplication: X * Y
Calculating the answer to this problem is a task that is very easy for a typical classical computer, no matter what values we choose to use for X and Y. A machine as feeble as a pocket calculator can do the necessary computations in mere fractions of a second. The same holds true if we make the factors involved even bigger. Adding more digits to the numbers involved in the calculation has little impact on the time or computing resources required to obtain the answer.

Because of this, we say that this sort of problem is 'tractable' for a classical computer. We can increase the size of the task without an exponential increase in the resources (memory; processing capacity; time) that we need to make available to do it.

There is, however, no easy way in which to do the calculation in reverse. If you start with a large number and want to know which prime factors you have to multiply together in order to get that exact number, then you quickly find yourself in a lot of difficulty.

Because there are a great many computational steps involved in finding the answer, it can take a classical computer a very long time to achieve. In fact, every digit you add to the size of the number you want to factorise, exponentially increases the time that it's going to take to find the factors.

Figure 2.27

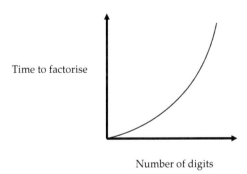

Time to factorise

Number of digits

We call this class of problems, 'intractable'. That is, we cannot continue to solve them trivially as the numbers involved grow larger.

At the time of writing, the worlds' most powerful supercomputer can execute about 93×10^{15} operations per second. That's a lot... But even at that staggering rate, it would take about six hundred thousand years to factorise a three hundred digit number.

We cannot even conceive of how to factorise a one thousand digit number using classical computers. And how on Earth might you deal with million, or billion digit numbers? There wouldn't even be enough time in the universe!

For this reason, the prime factors of very large numbers have been used as the basis of cryptographic technology for years. They are used to encode the content of the communications you have with people via your favourite secure messaging app on your phone, for example.

The encoding *can* be cracked, but it's going to take hundreds of thousands of years to do so... by which time, you're probably not likely to care an awful lot...

The app owned by the person with whom you are exchanging messages, by contrast, can decode them immediately. This is because your installation of it shares the correct factors with theirs in advance. Multiplying those factors together to get the larger number is lightning quick, and so you - and only you - can read each other's correspondence without having to wait several hundred millennia to do so.

Many forms of encryption used to secure military and government communications operate on a similar basis, because the factorisation of large numbers is an *intractable* computational problem.

Intractable, of course, for classical computers. But what if you could cheat? What if you could dramatically reduce the time required for the calculation by distributing the work across parallel timelines? Split the calculation across a sufficiently large number of alternate histories, then use interference to recombine the results and obtain your answer, and hey presto! You could potentially get your answers in virtually no time at all...

In 1994, the mathematician Peter Shor discovered an algorithm which does exactly that. For any given integer, it makes use of calculations spread across quantum superpositions to find its prime factors, and does so almost exponentially faster than the most efficient known classical method (an algorithm called the 'general number field sieve'). In 2001, it was demonstrated in practice by IBM, whose implementation performed the rather modest factorisation of the integer 15 (into the prime factors 3 and 5).

 In 2012, Shor's algorithm was used to factorise the number 21, but further progress has been limited by the difficulties of preventing the qubits from interacting with the environment, and decohering (thereby losing access to the superpositions upon which they rely).

The race has since been on to make the hardware catch up with theory, and address the practical problem of implementing large-scale suppression of superposition decoherence, which will allow for the construction of quantum computers with ever more qubits (and therefore ever more access to the resources of parallel histories).

Because of the current hardware limitations, the world of secure cryptography is not yet under immediate threat, but with the knowledge in place of how to do it given the hardware (progress on which is progressing continuously), it is considered only a matter of time.

The research continues, but the mere fact that we live in a world where we are (already... today...) exploiting the multiverse by distributing computational tasks across alternate histories, is probably rather surprising to most readers.

Collapse theorists would of course dispute that this is the true mechanism by which it works, though if the superposition has no physical reality (as they would maintain), it is not clear exactly where calculations such as those in Shor's algorithm are actually taking place.

Outside of reality, one would assume…

"To those who still cling to a single-universe world-view, I issue this challenge: explain how Shor's algorithm works. I do not merely mean predict that it will work, which is merely a matter of solving a few uncontroversial equations. I mean provide an explanation. When Shor's algorithm has factorized a number, using 10^{500} or so times the computational resources that can be seen to be present, where was the number factorized? There are only about 10^{80} atoms in the entire visible universe, an utterly miniscule number compared with 10^{500}. So if the visible universe were the extent of physical reality, physical reality would not even remotely contain the re-sources required to factorize such a large number. Who did factorize it, then? How, and where, was the computation performed?"[12]

David Deutsch

Marc Garner / NASA JSC

Valiant hearts,

Fear not the darkness,

Uncertain thy tread,

Though never alone...

Parallel Timelines, Choice & Reckoning

We turned to the inscrutable world of the quantum, in the hope of finding answers with regards the existential questions posed by the fact of living in a 4-dimensional and relativistic Spacetime block. We went looking for the origin of our experiential flow of time, but instead found a mystery deepened.

Rather than an explanation of why we find such dynamic and constant change in the changeless, we have thus far only succeeded in uncovering a vastly broadened arena of parallel histories in which the enigma of existence plays out.

Figure 2.28

Individual histories of the classical Spacetime block

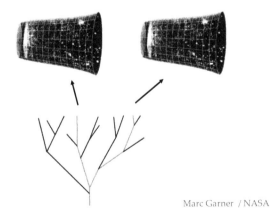

Web of parallel histories - 'The Multiverse'

Marc Garner / NASA

Whenever a quantum measurement event (i.e. any quantum interaction) happens, there is not any one single future that comes into being - they **all** do. Every possible measurement outcome actually comes to be, each leading to a new almost-autonomous history of the universe (branch of the universal wave function).

This is the natural consequence of the smooth and continuous evolution of the wave function by the Schrödinger equation. It is what happens when the bare quantum formalism is applied to the real world, without any hand-crafted add-ons (such as wave function collapse) being falsely manufactured to prevent it.

For every measurement event, the full spread of potential eventualities is actually realised.

E.g. If I measure the spin of an electron, then I am branched into different histories - one for each state of the electron's superposition with regards to its spin along my chosen axis. In each of those histories, I find a different (but definitive) value for the spin. All eventualities happen, just on different branches of the multiverse - that is to say, in different histories.

But just how many physically realized histories of the Spacetime block are we actually talking about overall? When we speak of 'Many Worlds', just exactly how many do we really mean?

I have referred to this vast ocean of parallel timelines rather affectionately as the 'infinite tree', due to the tree-like structure introduced by emergent branching, but is it truly infinite? Are we justified in picturing it as an arena of literally endless possibility? Infinity is a big number... If those possibilities really are infinite, then it would mean that the tree contains within it literally every possibly conceivable history - everything we could ever imagine happening, would actually be physically manifest somewhere across the immensity of creation.

The first thing to say on this issue is that the possibilities are limited to those which are allowed by the laws of physics. When a quantum measurement event occurs, the wave function splits only into branches representative of the different *possible* outcomes - not branches representing *impossible* ones.

In our example of determining the spin of the electron, the possible outcomes are 'up' and 'down', and there is a resulting branch in which each is true. There is no branch for the outcome being 'blue', because that wouldn't be in accordance with the laws of physics.

The second thing to say, is that if we assume both space and time to be very large, but finite, then the question becomes one of whether or not there are infinite possible outcomes to be had as the result of measurement events on a finite number of particles, or whether that number is unimaginably large, but nonetheless finite.

In the case of measuring electron spin, the number of branches created as a result of that particular measurement are clearly finite, but what of the more problematic issue of a measurement of position? Precisely how many possible outcomes are there when you choose to take your measurement in the position basis?

We have already seen that there is a minimal measurable spatial distance, which we call the Planck Length, so presumably space isn't arbitrarily divisible, right? And if there is a smallest possible chunk of space, then it follows that there must be a finite number of outcomes for a position measurement, because there can be only so many places (albeit a vast number) in which the particle could be.

This however, is not an issue that is settled definitively. The Planck Length represents the smallest distance that we could ever theoretically hope to discern - which is not necessarily the same thing as the smallest physical distance there can be. It is the limit to which our resolution of measurement could ever reach. To go beyond it and determine a shorter distance would require that we put so much energy into the measurement, that Spacetime would actually collapse at the point we are measuring, concealing the outcome from us in an ultra-condensed region we call a 'black hole' (we will encounter these properly in Part 3).

The spacetime of Einstein and Minkowski is modelled as a continuum. That is to say that it is not granular and discrete, but smooth and continuous. If this view is correct, then it would mean that space **is** arbitrarily divisible (whether we would ever be able to discern it with the necessary resolution or not). In this case, there would be an infinite number of branches resulting from each measurement of position.

So which view is correct? Is space arbitrarily divisible or not? Unfortunately this is one of those questions whose answer is currently beyond the scope of what we can say with absolute certainty. There is good reason though, to suppose that there is a limit to how far you can chop things up - that there is a smallest possible grain of space which can be divided no further, and we shall explore this further in Part 3, when we look at the problem of the quantisation of space. For our purposes here though, we can choose to duck the question of precisely how many branches there are, by taking the 'infinite' in 'infinite tree' to mean an incomprehensibly large number by human scales - one so large that we can for all practical purposes treat it as infinite.

Regardless of the precise number of branches in the multiverse, it's important to stress that its natural branching behaviour is something which happens as a result of *quantum* events - not classical or emergent ones. The issue is often confused with the mistaken belief that branching occurs directly as a result of conscious choice, but this is to over-simplify.

It is often argued, for instance, that in a world where all outcomes happen, we must necessarily be freed from the shackles of morality when faced with choice. The reasoning goes something along the lines of - 'If I am faced with the option of doing good or doing evil, it doesn't matter which choice is made because across the multiverse in its fullness, there is really no choice at all (as on one branch I do the good thing, and on the other I do the evil one), so why worry? Both things happen so it makes no difference'.

Let's call this the 'argument of moral irrelevance'.

Before we address it, it is perhaps useful to briefly recap on what we have previously covered on the issue of free will. It's important to remember that all of time exists all at once, and that our experience of it 'flowing' forwards in a linear fashion in accordance with Newtonian dynamics, is not the way the world really works. We instead need to think of events in Lagrangian terms, and consider the entire timeline all at once.

We (or 'versions' of us, depending upon how you think about it) exist at all points along our world-lines. At each of those points, we are engaging in decision-making through a process of top-down feedback called 'free will', through which we pro-actively intervene in the otherwise purely deterministic evolution of the environment. As all of time exists all at once, those interventions are all made concurrent with each other - that is 'at the same time', or 'timelessly'.

Our *experience* of life, on the other hand, plays-out in a Newtonian-like manner through our mysterious 'flow' of time. The situation is somewhat akin to living through a movie that we've already created. We made that movie timelessly, but have the experience of 'moving through' its frames in a linear fashion, living-out the experience of exercising our free will moment -by-moment. The choices we experience living through though, are immutable because we've 'already' made them in a non-linear way.

Regardless, it **was** us that made them, and each of those choices that we experience moment-by-moment **are** the original decisions that we took. In this way, they were choices that we were free to make, but from the perspective of a Newtonian 'flow' of time, have no option but to follow. Time, and our perspective on it, can be somewhat confusing, for sure…

If we then introduce the parallel timelines of the multiverse into the equation, then it is into this context that the question of moral irrelevance is properly set. It is the question of whether or not we can sensibly assign any sort of morality to our decisions, or whether it really doesn't matter because across the multiverse, all possible outcomes happen anyway.

Consciousness though, and the decisions which it makes, are emergent phenomena, and do not cause branching directly. The brain is chock full of quantum ingredients (about 10^{50} atoms), and it takes the co-ordinated effects of an entire series of quantum events amongst them, to constitute a thought or a decision. The wave function branches with every single one of those constituent events, none of which is solely responsible for the decision on its own.

When you approach a fork in the road, for example, it is not a simple case of reality branching into a small handful of alternatives accounting for the various choices you could make (left, right, turn around and go back, sit down and check the map, curse the fact that you're lost, etc.). While you are in the process of deciding, the *individual* atomic-scale events that form your very thought process cause reality to branch an incredible amount of times, and the world will have sprouted entire sub-trees during the course of even a single decision being made.

Furthermore, consider the amount of photons that strike you whilst all that is going on. We have interactions with billions of them every second, and each one of those interactions 'kicks-off' a new set of branches too. And it's not just the light, of course - it's the air, the rain, or any form of contact with anything constructed of quantum ingredients. The list is endless. They all cause branching events, and with each and every new event, we branch too.

At your fork in the road, there is not a world in which you go left and a world in which you go right. There are many, many worlds created by an unimaginable number of quantum events, and you branch into them all. In each of those worlds, you eventually go on to have accumulated enough quantum events in your brain that your decision can be considered to be made.

Figure 2.29 shows this in a much simplified form, with far fewer branches (and branching events) than is realistic. It shows Alice starting out by initiating the decision-making process in a single branch, and ending-up completing it in many. In different branches, she may (or may not) arrive at different decisions.

Figure 2.29

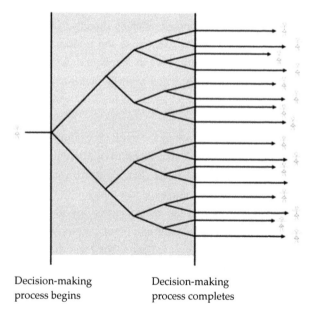

Decision-making   Decision-making
process begins   process completes

Let's follow the reasoning a little further. From our understanding of the world in Lagrangian terms, we know that pre-existing 'future' events exert an influence over the global profile of the timeline - helping shape the 'past' and 'present' into the reality we find. The same is of course true of events in that 'past' and 'present' - they help shape the overall timeline, and hence the future (this is obvious, even to our Newtonian-attuned minds!). Because of branching though, there is not just one future emanating from any given point, but many.

The world keeps on branching **after** a decision is eventually made too. So what a decision does do, is influence the shape of the Spacetime block in a great many timelines, as opposed to just the single one we are traditionally accustomed to thinking about. In figure 2.30, the timelines whose shapes are influenced by the decision arrived upon at point A, are highlighted in the lighter shade of grey. They include both what lies to the 'past' of point A, and what lies to its 'future'.

Figure 2.30

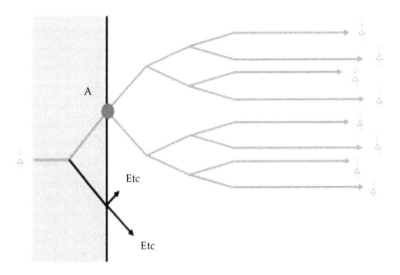

Decision-making
process completes

The fact that we live in a multiverse changes only the scope of the impact of our choices - not how we should think about making them, and it does not remove morality from the picture. In fact, I would argue that it's the complete inverse of the argument of moral irrelevance that's actually true. That is to say that, if anything, because of the branching our moral responsibility is not diminished, but increased. An act of kindness shapes not just one history, but an incomprehensible number of them. The same is true of an act of malice.

We also need to consider that when we are branched, we become many 'copies' of ourselves in parallel timelines. Each doppelganger goes on to make their own decisions, and while they have essentially become separate individuals, immediately after branching, they are to all intents and purposes identical. They share a common 'past', common beliefs, and common personalities. They share the same hopes; fears; joys; sorrows; passions; memories; and perspectives. Over time, differences will gradually build up in each of them (and in each of their worlds), making them more and more differentiated from each other, but their very nature is dictated by the nature of the person they branched from, and has a profound effect upon the choices they make immediately after their initial branching (at the very least), and arguably for the remainder of their world-lines.

We therefore each have a deep responsibility to act with compassion, humanity, and honour, for the scope and impact of both the decisions we make, and the dispositions of our characters, are in reality much wider than first meets the eye. With the static nature of the spacetime in which we exist, that scope and impact is also of course quite permanent - preserved in perpetuity in time, across branches, and lived-out eternally by us and the others with whom we share common moments.

There are an unimaginable multitude of ways in which history plays out, and our choices shape that immense landscape for good or for ill. Our other selves out there leading parallel lives in that vast ocean of reality, carry with them the essence of us, and both we and they should feel the weight of that great privilege and responsibility, as we strive to do what we can to act with nobility; to bring good into our worlds, and into those 'future' worlds to which ours give birth.

As I walked amid the souls a-plenty,

They took the paths I couldn't see,

The haunting truth in reason forming,

- Those spectres many,

They all were me...

...Shadow wraiths whose ghostly presence,

Through weight of chance defines the law.

Our exploration of the remarkable quantum underpinnings of our classical reality, has revealed an unexpected treasure in the fact that time is not only deep, but broad, and has provided a glimpse of the bewildering scale which that breadth really holds.

What it has not done (thus far) is to furnish us with the answers we seek regarding time's apparent flow, and how it's possible that we are able to think and perceive in a world in which nothing (including the electrical signals in our brains) ever moves. In many ways, with the realisation that there are an incomprehensible number of parallel versions of ourselves living-out alternate histories, it has in fact only served to render our questions even more acute.

We have nonetheless, in the concepts of superposition and entanglement, discovered some startling ideas that will prove to be of critical importance to us in our quest for understanding.

Superposition tells us that a quantum state consists of many different configurations which co-exist simultaneously - any one of which could manifest as an apparent measurement outcome to us when our world branches; and entanglement blurs the distinction we can reasonably draw between any given systems which have undergone an interaction.

They are ideas we will carry forwards with us, along with this picture of a relentlessly branching tree of histories, into the next stage of our journey, where we will encounter what are perhaps some of the strangest and most perplexing notions that the world has to offer.

We carry them forwards, into the realm of quantum gravity...

03:00

III – Quantum Spacetime

Marc Garner / Albert Barr / EpicStockMedia / shutterstock.com

Towards the perimeter,
At the edge of all knowledge,
To look to the void,
For to see...
For to know....

Falling

"Everything likes to live where it will age the most slowly"[13]

Kip S. Thorne

Through Einstein's theory of Special Relativity, and Minkowski's application of it to the geometry of Spacetime, we have a picture of a world where time is relative, and the concept of duration is not something which is fixed, but which is instead a dynamic and flexible quantity that is dependent upon your perspective and motion.

But as Einstein went on to show with his General Theory of Relativity in 1915, the revelations about the nature and role of time run yet deeper still.

It was more than two hundred years earlier that Newton had first concerned himself with the question of why things fall. The answer that he came to - that it is due to the force of gravity - was an astonishing and remarkable leap. But while the formula he produced provides a very good approximation of the *effects* of gravity, it falls short by way of *explanation*.

For Newton, gravity was a force much like any other. Though the mechanism by which it comes about was not known, it was assumed to operate in a manner akin to the other forces in nature. This was an entirely reasonable assumption, which Einstein showed to be utterly false. Gravity, as it turns out, could not be more **unlike** the other forces, for it is not really a *force* as such at all - it is the result of the curvature of the geometry of Spacetime itself.

As we have seen, when something moves through space, it does so along the path which has the lowest value for the 'action'. But space is not a fixed grid of places against whose rigid backdrop the world unfolds... With General Relativity, Einstein showed it instead to be a malleable mesh of inter-related distances and events. The stage upon which events play out is not simply a passive container of things - it is itself a dynamic actor whose shape and geometry is warped and deformed by the things it contains. It is warped and deformed by their mass.

In the vicinity of mass, time slows down. Time runs at a different rate on the surface of the Earth for example, than it does in the sky. It even runs at a different rate for your head than it does for your feet. This is because your feet are (generally) closer to the bulk of the Earth than is your head. In this particular case, the difference in the rates at which time passes is miniscule, but measurable nonetheless. Clocks accurate enough to record it are in fact relatively commonplace in science labs around the world.

In the places where time slows, the geometry of space responds by curving inwards, inclining itself towards where time is at its most tardy. When this happens, the paths of least action become 'bent', and the trajectories along which things travel curve.

This can be observed in action in the night sky. The image in figure 3.1 shows light which has been emitted from a distant galaxy being bent around the mass of an intervening galaxy, as it travels through the warped space created as a result of that second galaxy's mass.

Figure 3.1

ESA / Hubble & NASA

When light is focused by a mass in this way, we call it 'gravitational lensing', as the geometry of space is in effect channelling the light like a lens. It is of course not just light that is affected - nothing can escape the effects of the bending of Spacetime, because everything is in Spacetime.

The sort of curvature we are talking about is usually illustrated with the 2-dimensional depiction of a 'gravity well', as in that of the Earth below:

Figure 3.2

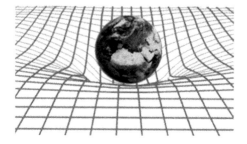

Marc Garner / creativestockexchange / shutterstock.com

This is partly due to it being easier to grasp the concept this way, but also because it is easier to draw! - A fact to which my attempt at a 3-dimensional illustration of it (in figure 3.3) probably attests... I shall certainly not attempt to draw it in four dimensions, but hopefully the idea is clear...

Figure 3.3

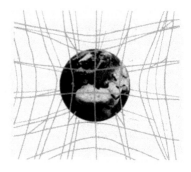

Marc Garner / creativestockexchange / shutterstock.com

In the words of John Wheeler - 'Spacetime tells matter how to move; matter tells Spacetime how to curve'[14]. It is this localised curvature of Spacetime which we experience as the 'force' of gravity.

If a ball falls when you drop it from a tower, it is due to it naturally following the geometry of space, which is sitting at an incline caused by a difference in the rate at which time passes between the top of the tower and its base. That time differential is in turn caused by the mass of the Earth, which is dilating time to differing degrees in different places, depending on how far away from it they are.

When you are pulled back to the ground by gravity after you jump towards the sky, it is the hidden hand of time which is pulling the strings and making you fall. It physically shapes the universe in which we live. It is only in the places where there is no time gradient that things do not fall; that they do not feel the incessant tug of gravity pulling at their core.

General Relativity reveals a world defined by a graduated and undulating landscape of time, which underlines and accentuates the key result of Special Relativity - that there is no universal time, and that past, present, and future are relative concepts in a pre-existing and block-like whole.

Even if everything in the universe were somehow able to move together in lock-step in the same inertial frame of reference, there would **still** be no universally identifiable plane of simultaneity. There would still be no one over-arching Now to rule them all, because time is slowed locally by the presence of mass. Every place has its own rate at which time is passing, and so every thing in the universe is marching through time to its own interminable and varying beat (in so far as anything moves in any sense at all, that is).

There is no collective time. There is nothing but the relations between the things of the world. A universe **is** these relations. It is the things it contains, and 'over time', it flexes and writhes to the rhythm of their interplay.

In the same year as Einstein published his great theory, it was read by a German soldier sitting in the world-war 1 trenches of the Russian front. This remarkable man, who had himself already had two papers on celestial mechanics published before he'd turned sixteen, was Karl Schwarzschild.

As the bullets rained down around him, on a scrap of paper he calmly sat and penned the first exact solution to Einstein's freshly announced field equations, and mailed it off to the great man himself.

In doing so, he drew attention to a bizarre prediction of the math, which are enigmatic objects known as 'singularities'. A mathematical singularity is a point at which a given mathematical object either ceases to be defined, or ceases to be well behaved. There is, for example, a mathematical singularity at the north pole of the Earth with regards to the concept of 'north' - you can move north until you reach it, but once there, there is no further north you can go. Any further movement from that point carries you away from north (even if you simply continue in a straight line). The singularities that we refer to in General Relativity are regions of zero volume, where the matter density, pressure, and Spacetime curvature are infinite, causing the laws of physics to break down, and the concepts of space and time to effectively come to an end.

For Einstein they were objects of concern, for he worried they were an indication that the theory was incomplete. Objects of zero volume yet infinite density seem so outlandishly improbable, that for many years they were viewed simply as mathematical curiosities that had no correspondence to any actual physical objects.

John Wheeler dubbed them 'black holes', due to the fact that within a certain surrounding volume, the force of their gravitational attraction would be so great that nothing which strayed too close could escape - not even light, leaving an area of complete darkness to enclose the singularity at the centre.

Despite the reservations of Einstein though (and much to the surprise of a great many), black holes have since been observed. They have been detected both indirectly through the influence they exert over their neighbours (such as stars being flung around at the centre of the galaxy, for example), and in 2019 directly, when the world was held mesmerised as the stunning first image of a black hole was published by an international collaboration using the Event Horizon radio telescope.

They are essentially the result of run-away gravitational collapse, which can occur as a result of the implosion of a star, for example.

It was to be forty years after Schwarzschild's initial discovery, before the implications of what he had found were to be properly understood, and those implications are extraordinary, for in the interior of a black hole, space and time switch roles...

This can be immensely difficult to imagine, but hopefully the following analogy will be helpful, and may also shed some light on the nature of the time-like dimension of Spacetime.

Instead of the four dimensions of the real world, for the sake of the analogy, we will make use of just three.

Let's suppose at this point, that they are all space-like dimensions., and that they allow for three different types of motion with regards to some imaginary axis, A.

Figure 3.4

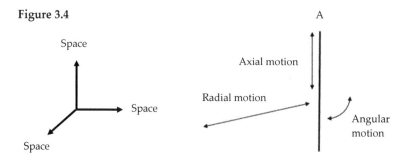

By combining these three types of motion (axial, radial, and angular), we can effectively move in any direction within the space.

Now let's introduce a few constraints to our little world here - let's say that an object isn't allowed to stand still, and that it must always include an upwards axial-motion component to its movements. Let's also say that any observers in the world cannot see anything along the axial direction, other than what lies along a plain intersecting the point of it at which they are located.

With those constraints, we have effectively turned our 3-dimensional space into a 3-dimensional spacetime, containing two space-like dimensions, and one time-like dimension, and the paths which objects follow now resemble world-lines, which are intersected by Now Slices:

Figure 3.5

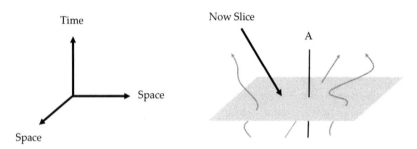

Radial and angular motions correspond to movements through 2-dimensional space, and axial motion corresponds to movement through time. An object which moves only in the axial direction, for example, would be standing still in the space and moving only through time.

Now let's introduce something else. Let's suppose there is a cylindrical surface centred about the imaginary axis in our model world, as follows:

Figure 3.6

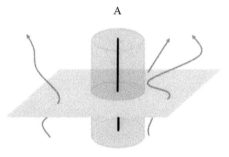

Let's say that everything outside of this surface behaves as we have described, but inside, something different happens - let's say that inside the cylinder, our constraints regarding the axial direction are discarded, and replaced with similar constraints with respect to the radial direction. So inside the cylinder, objects gain freedom in the axial direction, but lose it in the radial one - they must move inwards towards the axis.

Inside the cylinder, our radial direction has become time-like, and our axial direction has become space-like. Motion is allowed down the axis as well as up it, so long as there is a radial component towards it.

The arrows in figure 3.7 show the forwards direction of the time-like dimension in the 2 different regions of our space (inside the cylinder and outside of it).

Figure 3.7

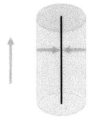

So for objects located outside of the cylinder, Now Slices are oriented as shown in figure 3.8:

Figure 3.8

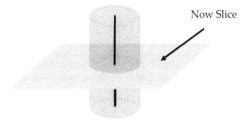

Now Slice

And for objects located in its interior, they are layered, like the skin of an onion:

Figure 3.9

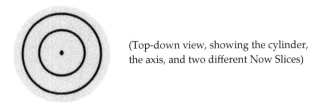

(Top-down view, showing the cylinder, the axis, and two different Now Slices)

Now let's call the axis a 'singularity', and the area inside the cylinder a 'black hole'. The surface of the cylinder is the 'event horizon', on the outside of which is ordinary space.

Let's consider the perspective of a person playing the role of an object in this toy universe, and think about what they would say the world is like. Let's pick on Bob...

Outside of the event horizon, Bob would report the singularity (pretending for a second that he'd be able to see it) to be a point in space that appears to have extension through time. As he crosses the event horizon though, everything changes. Things that were previously hidden from him by our constraints are suddenly visible - things which he would have previously thought about as being in the past and being in the future, are now all visible to him as residing at what are now space-like locations in his new type of present moment, as time is now flowing in the radial direction towards the singularity.

On the interior of the hole, the singularity itself no longer appears to Bob as a place that has extension in time, but is rather a future event (which he can't yet perceive), which will, when he reaches it, extend across all of space in one dimension inside the black hole.

Once he has entered the hole, there is no hope that he will ever exit, any more than there was ever any hope that he might travel backwards in time ('down' along the direction of the axis) in the ordinary spacetime on the outside of the horizon. He is doomed to move relentlessly forwards to the singularity.

Figure 3.10

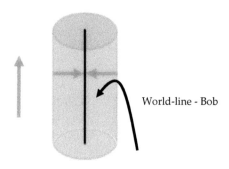

World-line - Bob

His world-line is shown in figure 3.10. It illustrates him crossing the event horizon, and plummeting inwards until he reaches the singularity. Notice that I have him moving down the axis once he is inside the hole. This is to illustrate that what was once the time direction for him (when he was on the exterior), becomes a spatial direction in which he has freedom to choose his direction once in the interior.

Once he reaches the singularity (the axis), there is nowhere left to go. He cannot progress any further in the inwards direction, and yet he must. The result is that he is consumed by the singularity. He becomes part of it.

There are numerous imperfections with this analogy, but hopefully it serves to make the remarkable disjunct between the space inside a black hole, and the space we are more used to on its exterior, a little more clear.

I hope too, that it illuminates something of our real 4-dimensional Spacetime, and perhaps sows the seed of the idea that the dimensions of space and time are maybe not so fundamentally different from each other as we might suppose. Could it be that the key distinguishing difference between them, is simply the obligation to move in a certain direction in one, while having freedom in the others?

In this idealised example, I simply arbitrarily introduced different constraints in the two different regions (inside and outside the hole), but what actually happens at the event horizon of a real black hole? How does the analogy transpose to the real world?

In our relativistic Spacetime, where both distance and duration are flexible quantities that bend and warp with regards to the observer, there is in fact something which still manages to remain constant in all frames of reference - something called the 'Spacetime Interval'.

This is a quantity which relates the spatial distance and the time interval between two events, and is what dictates causality. In mathematical terms, it is the 'distance' that lies between events in 4-dimensional Spacetime. While the spatial and temporal distances involved will vary depending upon your choice of frame of reference, the Spacetime Interval (the number representing the relation between those quantities) will not. It remains consistent, regardless of the frame of reference you are using.

In order to see why it is important, we can make use of one of Minkowski's great innovations - the Spacetime diagram. This is a way of graphically representing space and time which we first encountered in Part 1, and is of great use in visualising the differences in what is experienced by different observers (in different frames of reference).

Time is plotted along one axis, and for the sake of simplicity, just one dimension of space is plotted along the other.

Figure 3.11

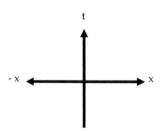

The axes are scaled such that the world-lines of rays of light are angled at 45^0, as shown in figure 3.12. If we take t=0 to be the 'present' moment, then those world-lines of light define the past and future 'light cones'. These are the regions of Spacetime in which events can have a causal influence involving any event at time t=0. Events which lie within the past light cone could potentially have had a causal impact upon what's happening at time t=0, which could in turn have a causal impact on anything located inside the future light cone.

Figure 3.12

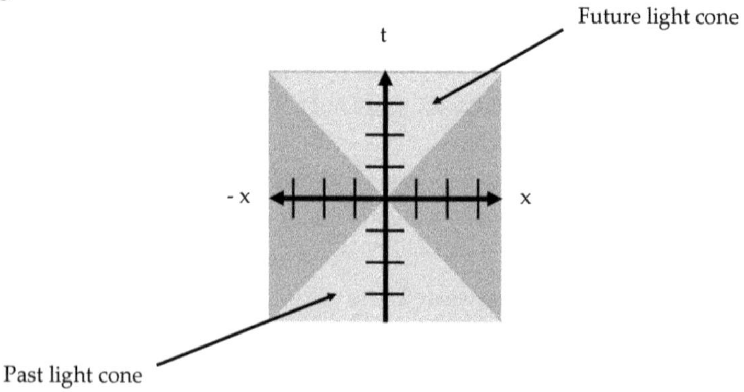

Future light cone

Past light cone

If Bob is 'stationary' in space, then his world-line is the vertical that runs along the time axis (because he has no motion in space, but is still moving forwards in time). Alice, moving through space (slower than the speed of light), has a world-line somewhere within the light cone:

Figure 3.13

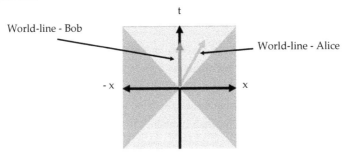

If they both measure out, say, three seconds according to clocks in their own frames of reference, then Alice's world-line is longer than Bob's (as shown in the figure 3.13). We could plot her motion for numerous different speeds she might travel at in either spatial direction, and if we indicated the 'three second mark' on each of her world-lines, we would see that they lie on a hyperbola, as shown in figure 3.14:

Figure 3.14

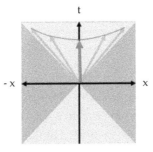

We could in fact do the same for any period of time, and obtain a set of hyperbola which represent the 'contours' of causality ('causality' being the relationship between cause and effect):

Figure 3.15

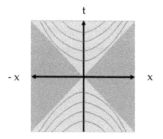

The gap between the contours, is the Spacetime Interval between those times. If the value of that interval is less than or equal to 0, then it is said to be time-like. That is to say, causal influences propagate through the temporal dimension in the manner to which we are accustomed. If however, the interval is positive (greater than 0), then it is said to be space-like, which means that causality propagates through space, rather than through time.

One way to achieve a positive interval would be if you could somehow travel faster than the speed of light (thereby reaching an area that lies on the outside of your light cones). Figure 3.16 shows regions with just such a positive interval relative to you.

Figure 3.16

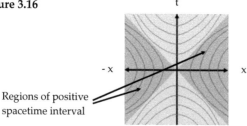

Regions of positive spacetime interval

In these regions the causal geometry is space-like, and the contours of causality are rotated. As it's not actually possible to travel faster than light, they remain inaccessible to the observer, but there is nevertheless a way for causality *within* the light cones to become space-like too. This can happen once you bring Spacetime curvature into the picture through General Relativity - if that curvature is of sufficient intensity, then a positive Spacetime Interval can be created within past and future light cones. This is, in fact, what happens inside the event horizon of a black hole.

There, the singularity is a future event, and the contours of causality are space-like. Light cannot climb out of them, and as it tries, it becomes trapped in layers that have to all intents and purposes, become time-like. They are Now Slices through which you are 'pulled' by gravity, as you fall inwards to the singularity.

The light through which you fall is that which was emitted during the collapse of the star. It is struggling to get out, without success. Your experience as you move radially through it, is one of falling into the deep past (which is now your future!). Meanwhile, light that has fallen into the black hole after you, can overtake you. Were you able to look up and see it, you would see what was the 'future' when you were on the outside of the hole, come tumbling past you. It falls at you from above - from what is now the direction of your past - and races beyond you into the new direction of your future, never to be seen again.

Black holes represent what are perhaps the strangest places in the cosmos, and are physical embodiments of General Relativity at its most extreme.

Between them, General Relativity and Quantum Mechanics form the two great pillars of modern physics. Together, they offer an exquisitely precise description of nature, with General Relativity explaining the workings of the emergent and macro-scale 'classical' world, and Quantum Mechanics elucidating the underlying interactions of the microphysics, and how they give rise to that classical world that we see.

Figure 3.17

Individual histories of the classical Spacetime block (described by General Relativity)

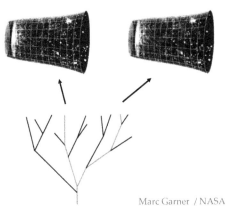

Web of parallel histories (described by Quantum Mechanics)

Marc Garner / NASA

Both theories have rigorously stood up to experiment, and have time and again proved to be correct. The difficulty is, that they do not sit easily besides one another. Everything except gravity can be relatively straight-forwardly taken into the framework of quantum mechanics, and 'quantised'. But when it comes to the gravitational field, things are not quite so 'simple'. We can quantise the electromagnetic field for example, for while it has EM radiation (photons of light) as its manifestation, that radiation exists in the context of Spacetime. It is *in* space, and it is *in* time. The gravitational field, by contrast, *is* Spacetime. It *is* space, and it *is* time.

Why should this be a problem? Well because the standard formulation of quantum mechanics requires an assumed 'background' flow of time against which the evolution of the wave function can be measured. So how on earth are you supposed to provide a quantum mechanical description of Spacetime, if you need an external time in order to do it? Time by definition, is an intrinsic part of Spacetime. It is internal to it. How do you describe the time-like dimension if you need time to already be in place first!?!

This is a difficulty which has historically been referred to as 'the problem of time' - We know that the world is quantum mechanical, and that Spacetime emerges from it, and yet quantum mechanics seems to require the pre-existence of time in order to work.

Figure 3.18

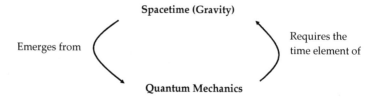

It is a resolution to this circular paradox, which the next two chapters are dedicated to exploring. It is one of the key issues, in the problem of 'quantum gravity'...

Upon the Earth the starlight falling,
Renders in the traveller's dream,
The world in which he so supposes,
To find himself alive and free...

Quantum Timelessness

&

The Previous Forever

"Other times are just special cases of other universes"[15]

David Deutsch

Any theory which seeks to rectify the disjunct between Quantum Mechanics and General Relativity, must not only overcome the 'problem of time', but must also provide an explanation of how Spacetime comes to be.

The theory (whatever it is) cannot be set *within* Spacetime, rather Spacetime must emerge as one of its consequences. This is a feature that is known as 'background independence', and any theory that does not have it, cannot be truly fundamental - a truth which is born of the fact that the gravitational field *is* the spacetime we are trying to quantise.

Early formulations of String theory for example, required Spacetime to pre-exist as the backdrop against which they played out. So remarkable though they may be (we are not going to explore them here), they could not be the ultimate answer because they were not background independent - they had a reliance upon space and time already being place.

For the purposes of *our* investigation, our interest (ultimately) lies in what time *is*, and where it comes from. So the understanding that we seek needs to be that more fundamental and background independent one. There are several competing candidates for what that understanding might be, and we will turn to them shortly, but first it is helpful to talk a little further on the topic of black holes, and the enigmatic singularities which they purport to enclose. This is because they are regions in which the melding of Quantum Mechanics and General Relativity have direct physical consequences, making them the ideal proving-ground against which aspiring theories of quantum gravity can be tested, and judged.

The gargantuan gravitational fields that are involved in black holes, emanate from colossal amounts of matter that have been crushed down to what General Relativity holds must be a single point of infinite density and zero volume - a singularity. If there's anywhere in the universe that the effects of extreme gravity operating at the quantum scale are most likely to be exposed, it is surely here. For good or for ill, the manner in which a theory of quantum gravity handles the issue of singularities, is one of the main yardsticks by which it will either live or die. This is because while black holes have been definitively observed in nature, whether or not singularities truly reside at their centres remains controversial, for it is one of the areas in which General Relativity and Quantum Mechanics make seemingly incompatible predictions.

Relativity tells us to expect a singularity, but Quantum Mechanics suggests that the gravitational field can not be so well defined as it would need to be in order for that to happen. So which is correct?

The infinitesimally small scale at which General Relativity tells us that singularities are expected to form, is precisely the scale with which Einstein's great theory is ill-equipped to deal. At such scales, quantum effects are instead expected to dominate, and the general belief is that in reality, quantum fluctuations of geometry will override gravity and prevent the singularities from forming. A good theory of quantum gravity, is therefore expected to be one in which singularities do not actually occur.

But if this view is correct, then how to account for the black holes that we see?

Well, the point is that matter densities and Spacetime curvatures could easily be of sufficient intensity to form black holes, without the necessity of singularities. During the collapse of a star, Spacetime reaches the point of sufficient density to form a black hole *before* everything is squashed down to the quantum scale. So a black hole could in theory form around a blob of extremely condensed matter, without that matter having to be crushed to infinity at a point of singularity.

It is an important issue, because it is not just the singularities of black holes that Einstein's theory predicts...

In 1927, a Belgian Catholic priest by the name of Georges Lemaitre used General Relativity to make the prediction of an expanding universe. He had observational evidence to back it up too, in the form of the 'red-shift' of what he termed 'extragalactic nebulae' - a class of objects which we know today to be other galaxies.

Red-shift is where the wavelength of the light emitted from stars becomes stretched, 'shifting' its colour towards the red end of the spectrum. Lemaitre postulated that it was in fact the stretching of space as it expanded, that was responsible - red-shifting the light from the nebulae as it moved them away from us in all directions. The universe, at the time, was thought to be constant in size, so the notion that it was expanding was something of a bold claim. It was however, observationally verified a couple of years later by the American astronomer Edwin Hubble, and forms the basis upon which Lemaitre's greatest insight was founded - that if the universe is expanding, then however the stars and nebulae might be positioned today, they must have been closer together in 'the past'.

In fact, if you are to take that argument to its logical conclusion, and use General Relativity to 'rewind' the evolution of the expanding universe as far as you can, then what you end up with is all of space, and everything it contains, compacted down into a single point of infinite density - a singularity.

It is the same physics as that of black holes, which gives us the prediction that the universe - and hence time itself - 'began' in a singularity demarking its initial boundary. It is this line of reasoning from Lemaitre which later developed into the much celebrated theory of the Big Bang - a theory which deals with how the universe might have suddenly inflated faster than the speed of light*, transforming from a point of infinitesimal size to about the

---

* The restriction that nothing can move faster than the speed of light applies only to that which is moving through space... there is no such restriction upon the speed at which space itself can grow.

size of an orange in less than a trillionth of a second, and to a diameter spanning thousands of light years just a short time later.

But if the suspicion is correct that quantum fluctuations would prevent such a singularity from actually forming, then there are serious cosmological implications, because the so-called 'singularity' of the Big Bang - the boundary that we have come to traditionally look upon as the 'beginning' of the universe (and the furthest back in time to which you can 'rewind the clock') might actually be nothing of the sorts.

Under this scenario, the Big Bang would not be so much of a bang, but more of a bounce - the result of a contracting region of space (or perhaps even the entire universe) caving in on itself (much as in the case of a black hole) and coming close to forming a singularity, but ultimately being overwhelmed by quantum fluctuations and forced to bounce outwards and re-expand.

The application of quantum ideas such as this to the large-scale structure and evolution of the universe is called 'Quantum Cosmology'.

Figure 3.19

Marc Garner / NASA

The traditional view

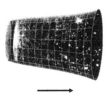

Expansion

The expectation of quantum cosmology

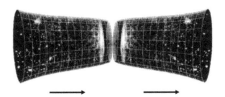

Contracting phase   Expanding phase

If correct, this would mean that in effect, there has been a 'previous' forever.

It's an intriguing picture which has its roots in Heisenberg's Uncertainty Principle, which says that the gravitational field cannot be so well defined as it would need to be at a singularity, and would instead be subject to fluctuations that would generate a bounce.

There are differing models of how this might happen. One is that the universe as a whole began contracting in a previous era, and continued to do so until it reached the point of a bounce. Others (called 'cyclic' models) have it progressing through endless such bounce-expansion-contraction-bounce cycles. My personal favourite though, is an idea which holds that when a singularity is close to forming, a structure called an 'Einstein-Rosen bridge' (popularly known as a 'wormhole') is actually created instead. This is a bit like a tunnel through space and time, which in this case links the highly compressed region at the centre of a black hole, to a newly forming region of space (on the other 'side' of the black hole) that has the diametric opposite characteristics. I.e. a region from which everything is ejected. Such (theoretical) regions are called 'white holes', and behave like black holes operating in time-reverse.

In this model, energy from the in-flowing space of the black hole, is squirted through the wormhole into the newly forming region of the white hole, from where it flows out. In other words, Spacetime doesn't bounce back into the region that it collapsed from, but into a new region altogether.

Tantalisingly, any life-forms which might evolve inside the space rushing away from a white hole 'singularity', would find that their Spacetime environment looked very much like an expanding universe that had started with a Big Bang.

Could this be what our universe is? Could our entire spacetime actually be the result of a white hole? Is that in fact what universes are? And are we witnessing their creation when we look at black holes? The physicist Lee Smolin suggests that we are - that deep within the bowels of black holes, new universes are being born through their own Big Bangs, and that this is precisely how our own came to be.

White holes are actually a prediction of General Relativity too (though not in the context of a bounce), and our universe *does* indeed look very much like them. All these models of cosmological bounces are just speculative though, and to unlock the answers to the remarkable questions they pose, we need a viable quantum theory of gravity to tell us exactly how Spacetime behaves under extreme compression.

One of the first and most momentous breakthroughs towards such a theory, was made in the 1960's by the great John Wheeler and his eminent collaborator - Bryce DeWitt.

The story goes that the two men had arranged to meet in an airport lounge, during a two hour stop-over that Wheeler had between flights. DeWitt turned up with two things - the first was a recently published equation for General Relativity which had been discovered by Asher Peres, and the second was the idea that it might be readily translatable into a wave equation for the gravitational field.

Right there and then, they set about the task of seeing whether it was possible, and in that briefest of sessions, successfully produced a formula describing the wave function of a quantised gravitational field.

Wheeler is said to have declared on the spot that *the* equation for quantum gravity had been found. As a charming aside, he preferred to call it 'the DeWitt equation' or the 'Einstein-Schrödinger equation', while DeWitt favoured 'the Wheeler equation'. Everybody else calls it 'Wheeler-DeWitt'...

But having an equation and knowing how to solve it are two quite different things, and knowing how to interpret the solutions once you have them, is yet another still. There are a number of deeply puzzling features of the equation, which have led to decades of confusion and debate - the most notorious of which, is perhaps the fact that it is completely and utterly devoid of any notion of time.

In a theory out of which you hope time (and space) will emerge, this lack of a pre-existing time upon which it is dependent, is of course exactly the sort of thing you might hope for. And yet it is not immediately clear how time might emerge from within it. Instead, it would seem to suggest that the universe exists in an un-evolving superposition of all of its geometries, all at once.

That is to say - not just a superposition of all the different geometries it might have 'at a given time', but of all its geometries across **all** time.

This would appear to be consistent with the idea that as time is an internal feature of the universe, then there is no external clock against which it can evolve as a whole. There is no time in the equation because there is no time outside of Spacetime, against which its evolution can be measured. So it seems to be describing the universe overall, as it would appear to an observer located on the 'outside'. That is, as eternal, timeless, and static.

There are deep echoes here of how all of time exists all at once in the classical picture, where all moments exist on an equal footing, and the paradox of how that might translate to a dynamical picture when viewed from within, is echoed too.

The absence of time from the equation accounts for the overall static nature of the universe, but how do you then account for the 'background' time component that is so critical to standard quantum mechanics? How do you account for the perceived evolution from the perspective of an observer internal to the universe?

These are very difficult questions, hence the decades of confusion and the difficulties in understanding how to properly interpret what the equation is saying.

From the 'inside' perspective, we obviously do not experience the world as being in a superposition - we instead find it to be in very distinct states. Everett had of course already provided an explanation for why this is (that it is due to the fact that we entangle with the world, and in doing so lose our ability to perceive the other components of the superposition), and perhaps this was one of the reasons why DeWitt was moved to adopt the Many Worlds point of view.

But here we have more than just different states that exist 'at the same time' - we have them across all time, so there is an additional dimension to the picture.

As would be later pointed out by David Deutsch, those states can be thought of as representing the universe at different 'snapshots' that are akin to 'moments', and that those which we somehow experience as sequential evolutions in the same history (even though they really exist all at once in superposition), are not particularly different in character from those which exist in parallel on different branches.

Consider the segment of the Multiverse shown in figure 3.20.

Figure 3.20

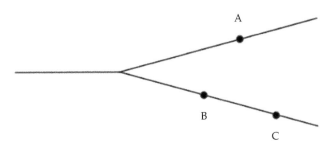

Here we see two branches, representing two divergent histories. Points A, B, and C, represent states of the static 3-dimensional space at particular moments.

Taken as singular instants, they can be viewed as essentially being different 'snapshot' universes. The only thing that makes point A different in character from points B and C, is that B and C can be placed into the same history, whereas A cannot.

What we think of as being different times in history then, are really just special cases of different snapshot universes, where the evolution of the system can be placed into the same timeline.

But is any of this correct?

Fortunately, there is a way to at least give an indication as to whether or not the overall quantum state is static, and whether the equation is therefore pointing us in the right direction. This is due to the fact that it tells us that there are no genuine dynamics, which in turn means that the overall energy content of the universe must be zero. This is because in Quantum Mechanics, the rate of change of the wave function is related to how much energy the quantum system has, and if it is un-evolving, then that energy must be zero.

If the total energy of the universe did indeed turn out to be zero, then while falling short of proof that the math of Wheeler and DeWitt is correct, it would certainly give a strong indication that it is in fact so.

So does the universe actually have zero total energy? To help answer that question, finding a resolution to the related (but relatively more straight-forwards) puzzle of the large-scale topology (shape) of the universe, is of interest. There are essentially three categories into which the options fall - open, closed, or flat.

Figure 3.21

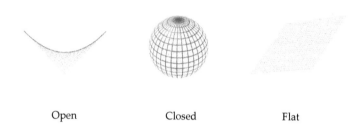

| Open | Closed | Flat |

Closed spacetimes are shapes which have an overall positive curvature, such as the sphere in figure 3.21, or a donut-shaped torus, for example. A spacetime of this nature has a positive energy density (has a greater than zero overall amount of energy), which is in contrast to open spacetimes, which have a negative energy density (a less than zero overall amount of energy).

Flat spacetimes however, allow for zero total energy. This is because the positive energy provided by matter, can be perfectly balanced by the negative energy of the gravitational field.

There have been a number of satellites that have been launched with the task of probing this question of the universe's overall large-scale topology. They are the WMAP, BOOMERanG and Planck satellites - veritable orbiting laboratories, all bristling with instruments designed to get to the bottom of this mystery.

Encouragingly, the experimental data they have provided lends strong support for a flat topology, with all of them independently suggesting that the universe is flat to within a margin of error of just 0.04%.

This is far from conclusive evidence of the universe having zero total energy, but is nonetheless highly suggestive.

The Wheeler-DeWitt equation does not in itself constitute a full-blown theory of quantum gravity, but it is widely considered to be a critical step along the road, and today constitutes the cornerstone of most serious attempts at the discovery of such a theory.

The world, it is generally believed, is at its most fundamental level a timeless quantum superposition of all of its states, all at once. The 'problem of time' is neatly side-stepped by virtue of the fact that time doesn't really exist, meaning the time parameter in the Schrödinger equation must actually be representative of some variable internal to the universe, which somehow mimics for us the role which we ordinarily attribute to time.

Precisely how this is done, and how the level of reality with which we are familiar arises from the timeless overall state, is to this day, a matter of intense competition between rival theories. The testing-ground of black hole physics is the rock against which they break themselves, and we shall explore some of the leading candidates in closer detail in the next chapter.

Through its relation,

The world...

On the Origins of Space

"As usual, nature's imagination far surpasses our own..."[16]

Richard Feynman

Modern theories of quantum gravity today take for granted that reality does not consist of a single spacetime, but of a superposition of many spaces which co-exist timelessly. This, they owe in large part to the Wheeler-DeWitt equation. With its description of a wave function of geometries, it has provided the conceptual framework in which such theories are set. None of them are yet free of flaws of one description or another, but neither are they yet complete.

The work here is ongoing, unfinished, and speculative. It represents the cutting-edge of modern physics, which it is hoped will one day yield that much sought-after full unification of the worlds of the quantum and the classical, and in doing so, provide the underlying explanation for the existence of space itself.

Here we take a brief sojourn to explore some of those remarkable theories, and see what insights can be gained that may help us in our quest.

We start near the beginning, with a theory born directly at the hands of John Wheeler himself - Quantum Geometrodynamics.

Quantum Geometrodynamics

'Geometrodynamics' is a synonym for General Relativity meaning 'the dynamics of geometry', so the name 'Quantum Geometrodynamics' is hence a reference to its (attempted) quantisation. It is also reflective of the fact that, in having the Wheeler-DeWitt equation at its heart, it describes the world in terms of a superposition of 3-dimensional geometries.

The approach taken was to attempt to quantise General Relativity directly, working backwards from the classical theory in search of its quantum analogue, and the result was one of the first fully-fledged attempts at a theory of quantum gravity.

Each eigenstate of the universal superposition is taken to be a 'hyperslice' of space, which is a very similar concept to that of Now Slices, except that at the quantum level there is no real time separation between each slice, because there is no time.

In the absence of time, questions about the 'evolution' of the geometry in the theory, are phrased in terms of what the volume of the space is in any given state. I.e. asking what the world is like in the state with volume X (actually the logarithm of the volume X, to be precise), is a bit like asking what the world is like at time X. So the time-ordering of events is in this way replaced with the evolutionary ordering of states, with the volume of space within those states playing the role of an intrinsic time parameter.

The result was a theory which reproduced dynamics that were in agreement with Einstein - unfortunately, too much so. Rewinding the internal 'time-evolution' of the states back to the big bang/bounce, regrettably resulted in the classic singularity of General Relativity. The theory in its original guise, although background independent, failed to avoid the break-down of physics under the extreme conditions of the 'early' universe, and favoured a bang rather than a bounce.

It remains an active area of research to this day, and some of the early setbacks have since been overcome, but it currently occupies a status as being somewhat lagging behind what has become one of the leading contenders - Loop Quantum Gravity.

Loop Quantum Gravity

It was the mid 1980's when the mathematical genius of Abhay Ashtekar, along with the visionary brilliance of Carlo Rovelli and Lee Smolin, found a solution to the Wheeler-DeWitt equation which seemed to describe closed quantum loops.

These loops, timeless and mysterious, were puzzled over until it was realised they could actually be loops of the field lines of the gravitational field, no less. This speculation heralded the birth of a new theory - 'Loop Quantum Gravity'.

Under this theory, the looped field lines of the gravitational field are interleaved to form something resembling a chainmail mesh.

Figure 3.22

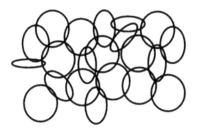

It is the points where the loops intersect (called 'nodes') that are the most interesting, for remarkably, what emerges is that these points are mathematically equivalent to volume. I.e. the physical volume of space might reside in the intersections of these conjectured loops of the gravitational field, without which, space would have no volume. Each node contributes a certain amount to the overall volume of space - they are postulated to be the discreet quanta of space, and are a billion, billion times smaller than the most tiny of atomic nuclei.

Being quantum mechanical, they are subject to the usual quantum laws, and may only take certain discreet values. As there is a minimum such discreet value they can have, then it follows that there is a smallest chunk of space which can exist. This is a departure from the Einstein-Minkowski picture of space, because it means that it is not continuous. There is in other words, a limit to how far it can be divided - there is a smallest possible grain of space which can be divided no further. This changes the picture from one of a continuum, to one of discreet granules which are linked together.

The sections of loop between these magical nodes of volume, serve as links between them, and in this manner, a sort of 'graph' emerges:

Figure 3.23

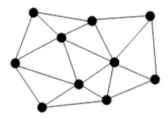

While the nodes give rise to volume, the links are what give rise to the physical property of 'area'. Between them, it is volume and area which give space the classical spatial characteristics with which we are familiar.

This network does not reside in Spacetime - it **is** the physical construct which *underlies* Spacetime. It is not in any place or time, rather it *defines* the concepts of space and time from within. It is the entity from which Spacetime emerges.

With regards to time, each node (being governed by a solution to the Wheeler-DeWitt equation), is itself timeless and eternal, with all of its many physical states existing all at once in superposition. The nodes and the network which they form do not evolve over time - they cannot, for they don't exist within time. The concept of time rather, emerges intrinsically as differences between the various states of each node.

The theory is hence fully independent of the Spacetime background, which in generates inherently from within.

There is in fact much that it has going for it. When the 'time evolution' of the world it describes is followed backwards to the 'beginnings' of time, the

Big Bang singularity of General Relativity is avoided, and the universe is successfully found to bounce. This distinguishes it as being perhaps the most mature theory of quantum gravity that we have. That is not necessarily to say though, that it is correct.

In 2009 it was unfortunately dealt a major blow when one of its predictions was tested through experiment, and found wanting. This was the forecast that high-energy EM radiation would be impeded on its journey through space, as it was slowed by its expected interaction with the inherent graininess of the proposed spacetime. This prediction was unfortunately falsified by looking for differences in the arrival times of light from deep-space gamma ray bursts, and failing to find them.

So we know that at the very least, some of the details of the theory are not correct - and perhaps more. This is the frustrating nature of what is commonly termed as 'the hardest problem in physics' - the problem of quantum gravity. Future research may well yield new insights which allow this setback to be overcome, but while theorists grapple with how that might be done, there are other ideas which are rapidly gaining support...

The Holographic Principle

The fact that blackholes mercilessly hoover up everything and anything that strays too close, causes a certain problem from the perspective of information in quantum theory. This is because quantum theory holds that much like energy, while quantum information may be converted from one form to another, it can **never** be destroyed. Black holes however (at least at first glance), seem to do precisely that.

By 'information', we mean information as termed in the scientific sense. This was formalised in 1948 by the American mathematical engineer, Claude Shannon, and is defined in terms of the number of possible alternatives for something.

If I know that it's April, for example, but I don't know which day, then when you tell me it's the 26th I gain information to the value of 30 (because there are thirty possible days in April that it could have been, and I have learned one that it is, and twenty nine that it is not). We say this represents five 'bits' of information (4.91 to be precise), because I could in theory have worked out which day it was by asking you no more than five yes/no questions. I.e.

'Is it later than the 15th?' - yes
'Is it later than the 23rd?' - yes
'Is it later than the 27th?' - no
'Is it later than the 25th?' - yes
'Is it the 26th?' - yes

So knowledge of which particular day in April it is, has information content thirty, which can be represented in five 'bits'.

As I've already mentioned, information can ordinarily only be changed from one form to another - it can never be destroyed. An example is the information that is stored in the pages of this book. If we had sufficient precision to track and control every particle of which the book is made, then even in the event of it being vaporised in a nuclear explosion, the laws of physics would allow us to (theoretically at least) reconstruct it afterwards, and piece the information back together.

In the case of matter, the information associated with it is encoded by the quantum properties of its particles.

The issue with black holes, is that anything which crosses the event horizon, though continuing to exist inside the black hole, is seemingly forever cut-off from the universe at large. While this is not necessarily a problem in and of itself, the fact that the hole subsequently evaporates away through a process known as 'Hawking Radiation' (so-named after its discoverer - the much celebrated Stephen Hawking, in the 1970's), most certainly **is**. Though the process of this evaporation is painfully slow (it might typically take place over time-spans much greater than the current age of the universe), once it is complete, there is no trace remaining of either the black hole, or the colossal amounts of information it swallowed up. All that remains is the scattered remnants of the Hawking Radiation emitted over the aeons from the event horizon. So where then, is the information embodied by the things which fell in? If it cannot be destroyed, then once the black hole has evaporated, where has it gone?

Black holes though, are inherently strange beasts, and all is not as it first appears...

In the early 1990's, the physicists Leonard Susskind and Gerard 't Hooft discovered that the mathematical description of a black hole's 3-dimensional interior space, is completely equivalent to the mathematical description of its 2-dimensional event horizon.

There are some truly magical things which this entails. We shall see first how they resolve this problem of apparent information loss, and then how they have profound implications for the possible nature of the world.

Due to intense time dilation, from the outside perspective the event horizon is a region where time actually stops (or more accurately, it is a place where a distant observer sees events take an infinite amount of time to play out). Because of this, information from the in-falling matter is effectively 'imaged' as it crosses over the horizon.

To see why, consider the case of Alice taking a wrong turn and accidentally steering her rocket across an event horizon. From her perspective, time keeps on running as usual, and she begins plummeting in towards the (supposed) singularity. According to Bob though, watching on in horror from afar, she never actually crosses that black hole's boundary - he instead witnesses her freeze in time as she hits the horizon.

So from her perspective she is inside the black hole, and from his she is not. The truth, is that both accounts are true. She is at once both in the interior, yet also 'imaged' at the horizon. In this way, the situation is much akin the manner in which information about a 3-dimensional hologram is encoded onto the 2-dimensional surface from which it is projected. There is (2-dimensional) information about her smeared across the event horizon, and there is the fully-fledged (3-dimensional) version of her in the black hole interior.

In this way, her information is not really lost to the universe at large in the first place, but instead remains locked into the event horizon - thereby side-stepping the feared information loss. Susskind and t'Hooft were able to go on to show that it is subsequently imprinted onto the out-going Hawking Radiation (eventually), and returned to the universe from whence it came.

Under this mechanism, even if it turns out that wormholes lurk at the centres of black holes, pushing information into a new baby universes, that information is not lost to the worlds from which it came.

The imaging (or put another way - 'duplication') of the information which this process relies upon, at first appears to violate the quantum No-Cloning theorem. This is another rule about quantum information, which states that it cannot be duplicated. Again though, not all is as it first appears. While a copy of the information most definitively **is** made, the situation re the No-Cloning theorem is rescued by virtue of the fact you can only ever access one or the other of the copies. I.e. You can remain outside of the event horizon and access a scrambled form of it (eventually, after many billions of years) via the Hawking Radiation, or you can cross the event horizon and have access to the 3-dimensional version on the interior.

If the story stopped there, it would already be remarkable. However, the significance of the fact that there is this strange sort of duality to black holes - that they can be completely described by either their surface or their interior, runs considerably deeper. Consider, for example, what suppositions we might naturally make about the upper limit of the amount of information that can be stored in a black hole. If we knew nothing of this duality, it would be perfectly reasonable to suppose that the maximum it can hold is however much information can be crammed into the volume of the interior. Yet this would be wrong. If the descriptions of the interior and the surface (the event horizon) are equivalent, then the amount of information that can be stored is naturally limited by whichever is smaller - and that is the surface. This is born-out by the math. The amount of information a black hole can store, is the amount that can be crammed onto the surface of the horizon - not how much could fit into the volume of the interior.

When it 'feeds', a black hole grows in volume by precisely the amount necessary for its surface to be able to store the additional information about the in-falling matter. In fact, it ends up storing one bit of information per Planck Area of its surface.

This means that some of our common-sense ideas about things, are again way off the mark. For example, the idea that the content of a black hole might determine its volume, which might define its surface area, which might in turn fix the amount of information that the surface can hold, is misleading.

This entire set of relations could in fact be more accurately viewed as operating the other way around. The information at the horizon can be said to actually *determine* the surface area that is required to store it. This in turn *defines* the volume of the interior, in which the nature of the things it contains is *defined by* the nature of the information at the horizon.

In other words, we can view the information at the event horizon as being more fundamental than the space it encloses. We can in fact see it as *giving rise* to the space of the interior, and all it contains. When Alice 'crosses' the event horizon, it is the information that gets imprinted onto it that is the more fundamental. The 3-dimensional Alice on the inside, is defined by it.

This became known as the 'Holographic Principle', and amazingly, Susskind and t'Hooft were able to demonstrate that in theory, it should apply just as equally to **any** space - not just that of a black hole.

The space inside a black hole (although twisted and warped) is, afterall, still just space. If it can be described purely in terms of a lower-dimensional surface that surrounds it, then perhaps so too could the 'ordinary' space we inhabit. It's an intriguing possibility - could our everyday 3-dimensional space actually be a strange form of holographic projection? Could it arise from the information that is 'stored' on its boundary?

Susskind and t'Hooft were able to demonstrate that at least in principle, this ought to be true.

One of the first obstacles to proving such a thing, is the question of what the boundary of our universe is actually like. We have already encountered the question of what the large-scale topology of the universe is, and discovered that there are three options - open, closed, or flat. The data we have from satellites designed to probe this question, indicates that it is most likely flat, although the issue is not settled definitively (while we see it as flat, it's still possible it's just so large that it just *seems* flat as far as we are able to see - much akin to the way that an ant is unlikely to be able to discern the overall curvature of the Earth).

This issue of topology has importance to the question of boundaries because two of the three options ('open' and 'flat') are infinite, and it's therefore not immediately obvious how such spacetimes might even *have* a boundary upon which 'holographic' information could be encoded.

Perhaps surprisingly though, it turns out that we *can* define boundaries for infinite spaces - at least mathematically. This is done by 'compactifying' the co-ordinate system of the space towards its boundary. As the boundary is approached, the more infinitely 'compactified' the co-ordinates become, hence rendering that boundary an infinite distance from any point on the interior.

The artist, M C Escher famously popularised the math behind this concept with his quite frankly genius series of 'circle limit' wood carvings, in which he depicts a conformally compactified hyperbolic ('open') space, tessellated with infinitely repeating elaborate patterns, the likes of which only he could conceive. My personal favourite, 'Circle Limit IV (Heaven and Hell)', is shown in figure 3.24. The tiles represent regions of space that are of equal size, beautifully illustrating the concept of infinite compactification as you near the boundary. Wherever you are located within the space, the boundary looks the same. Nobody is suggesting that real space is actually tiled with angels and demons, of course, but I think the visualisation helps to convey what is otherwise a quite mind-boggling concept.

Figure 3.24

Circle Limit IV (Heaven and Hell) - M C Escher

Someone who clearly needs little assistance with visualising it though, is Argentinian physicist Juan Maldacena, who in 1997 took this sort of thinking and used it to demonstrate the Holographic Principle in action at the cosmological scale. He did so in just such a hyperbolic (open) spacetime.

He was able to show that the interior of the space (the 'bulk') and its boundary, could be treated as completely equivalent and yet separate spacetimes in their own right - much like the descriptions of the interior of a black hole and its event horizon.

Incredibly, he came to this completely independently of Susskind and t'Hooft, of whose work he was not aware. While their work generalised the case of a black hole to *any* space in a somewhat speculative manner, Maldacena's was the first concrete realisation of the Holographic Principle applied at the cosmological scale, and was grounded in a mathematical rigour so complete that it could not be disputed.

His work was remarkable for many reasons, but perhaps the most spectacular among them was that the boundary of the space was defined by an everyday quantum field theory (which has nothing to do with gravity), and yet the bulk was a fully-fledged spacetime - gravity included.

By being 'projected' onto a higher dimensional space, the quantum field theory of the lower dimensional boundary, miraculously made gravity quite naturally 'just appear' in the bulk.

His discovery, is known as the 'ADS-CFT correspondence'. 'ADS' stands for 'Anti-De Sitter Space', which is the formal name for the open-shaped space of the interior, and 'CFT' stands for 'Conformal Field Theory', which is the formal name for the quantum theory of the boundary.

As we have already seen, our actual spacetime is most likely flat (and definitely not an Anti-De Sitter space, which would require a negative cosmological constant where ours is positive), so while Maldacena's breakthrough does not describe the real world, it is thought by many to nonetheless point the way towards uncovering the great mystery of how gravity can emerge from quantum mechanics. I.e. that it occurs in a space that is a sort of holographic projection of quantum information encoded on a distant boundary.

Hyperbolic space lends itself more readily to the mathematical analysis required to realise the Holographic Principle, but work is underway to attempt to generalise that result to flat spacetimes too.

The AdS/CFT correspondence is actually a background-independent realisation of the Wheeler-DeWitt framework, and in 2008 it was shown by Laurent Freidel that it could be derived directly from the Wheeler-DeWitt equation itself.

The picture was developed further when in 2010, the physicist Mark Van Raamsdonk demonstrated the crucial role played by entanglement in this strange duality between the theories of the boundary and the bulk. What he was able to show, was that as entanglement at the boundary was reduced, the bulk began to warp and deform as regions of space began to pull away from each other - stretching out like chewing gum being pulled from opposite ends.

Figure 3.25

If the entanglement is reduced sufficiently, then the regions actually separate.

Figure 3.26

And you can go further still - if you remove entanglement from the boundary altogether, then the space inside breaks up completely into tiny isolated grains. Conversely, as you begin to add entanglement back in, the space begins to weave itself back together. Individual grains of space behave as though they are a projection of what is happening at a lower-dimensional horizon, and entanglement within that horizon would seem to be the glue which binds them together - at least in the context of Anti-De Sitter space.

Exactly how this is applicable to our real spacetime remains to be seen. Behind that question, lies the sentiment that quantum information could in fact be more fundamental than even space and time.

Most contributors to the field do think that this is in fact telling us something deep and important about the nature of the real world, even if there is little agreement yet on precisely how the result translates to the true space in which we live. The evidence is slowly mounting, bit-by-bit (and from various directions of enquiry), that the universe can be understood in terms of quantum information processing.

In fact, work is currently underway to explore a striking correspondence between the growth of the complexity of quantum information, and the expansion of the universe. The outcome could turn out to be another step on the road to the gradually dawning realisation, that the universe (and everything it contains) may be nothing more than the holographic projection of information that is encoded in the entanglement of what sits at a distant horizon.

Entropic Gravity (A.K.A. Emergent Gravity) & MOND

When Newton's laws of gravitation failed to accurately predict the correct orbital path of the planet Mercury, almost two centuries passed before Einstein was able to successfully replace them with a theory that matched with observation - the theory of General Relativity. The anomaly in Mercury's motion was only slight, but the shift in the understanding that was required to account for it, was seismic.

It is the fact that the fabric of Spacetime itself is dragged around by the motion of the Sun, that is to blame, and this could never have been accounted for by Newton's laws, because they treat space and time as a fixed background.

There are certain gravitational phenomena in the universe though, for which even General Relativity cannot fully account for on its own. They are anomalies, if you will, in just the same sort of manner that the orbit of Mercury was. The structure of galaxies, is one such example. Because of the speed at which they rotate, galaxies really ought not to be able to hold onto their stars, which should fly apart and escape because there is not enough (visible) mass in the galaxy to combat the centrifugal force of the rotation - and yet they do not.

In order to explain this, it is ordinarily assumed that there must actually be more mass present than we can readily see. If true, then because we are unable to detect it (other than through the effects of its gravitation), we know that the source of that mass must be a novel form of matter constructed of particles with properties very different to the ones with which we are familiar. It must interact only very weakly with 'ordinary' matter (perhaps *only* through its gravitation), and it must effectively pass straight through everyday material. It must be completely translucent, and must exist in vast quantities throughout the cosmos. In fact, it must be five times more abundant than the regular matter that we know.

This is the famed 'dark matter', popularised through many modern articles and documentaries. There are numerous experiments that have been designed in attempts to detect it, but perhaps due the difficulties created by its stubborn refusal to interact with ordinary matter, it has thus far evaded confirmation. Perhaps the most well-known of these experiments is the Large Hadron Collider at Cern, Switzerland, which famously found the Higgs Boson in July of 2012. Amongst other things, it was also hoped it might detect a raft of 'supersymmetric' particles that are a prediction of String theory, and which were thought by many to be strong candidates for the particles of which dark matter might be constructed.

This possibility, though not yet completely ruled-out, is looking increasingly unlikely, as the energies at which these particles were supposed to exist have been extensively probed, and nothing has been found. Another dark matter candidate is a hypothetical class of particles called 'WIMPs' (Weakly Interacting Massive Particles). If they exist, then it is thought they would produce neutrinos (which are known particles that interact only through gravity and the weak nuclear force) when they annihilate through collisions with each other. It's believed that dark matter ought to be attracted to the mass of ordinary matter, and therefore accumulate in places such as the centres of stars. If so, and if WIMPs are the correct answer, then we could perhaps detect dark matter indirectly by looking for unexpectedly high numbers of neutrinos coming from the direction of the Sun. An experiment called 'IceCube' based at the Amundsen -Scott South Pole Station in Antarctica, does just that. Again though, there's as yet no indication of success.

No experiment, in fact, has ever made a convincing detection of dark matter to date. The general belief is that this will change, but there is one theory which takes another approach, and seeks a solution to the problem of galaxy rotations which doesn't involve dark matter at all - a solution which does the unthinkable, and seeks to modify General Relativity itself.

That theory is called 'MOND' (MOdified Newtonian Dynamics), and holds that when gravity becomes very weak (at approximately twelve trillionths of the strength of the gravitational field at the Earth's surface), it diverges from its classically understood nature. Specifically, it claims that around that threshold, the strength of gravitational attraction begins to fall-off linearly rather than according to the inverse-square law that it otherwise follows. Over cosmological scales, this would mean that gravity would not be as weak as predicted across an object the size of a galaxy, for example, and could actually provide an explanation for why they do not fall apart. If correct, then (in the case of galaxy rotations, at least) there would be no need to invoke the mysterious and elusive dark matter of standard theory.

The underlying framework for MOND is provided by something called 'Entropic Gravity' (a.k.a. 'Emergent Gravity'). This is something that is closely related to the concepts of the holographic approach, with which it shares a lot in common. Its philosophy is in recognising that the world is quantum from the start. Most approaches to the quantisation of gravity don't do this. Instead, they start with the classical theory and attempt to convert it to the framework of quantum mechanics. Loop Quantum Gravity for example, begins with a gauge theory formulation of General Relativity and seeks to quantise it from there. But we know that classical Spacetime emerges (somehow) from the quantum, so Entropic Gravity comes at the problem from the other end - by starting with the quantum and seeing if we can discover how Spacetime, and the structure and beauty of the world arise naturally from within it.

Much like the holographic approach, it holds that the key lies in entanglement, but there are some essential differences. Firstly, in this theory it is entanglement within the bulk itself which holds the key, and secondly, the domain it describes is that of a De Sitter space. The domains of De Sitter space are those of 'closed' and 'flat' spacetimes. (Recall that 'flat' is thought to be the most likely candidate for the topology of our actual spacetime).

It is based upon a type of entropy called 'entanglement entropy', which is purely quantum mechanical in nature, and provides a measure of entanglement between different sub-systems of a wave function. This is important because it allows for the relationship between information and area that was discovered through the study of black holes (I.e. that the area of an event horizon is defined by the quantum information that it holds), to be re-cast in terms of thermodynamics (entropy).

Using this, we can picture the wave function of the universe decomposed into an arbitrary number of sub-systems that are entangled with one another. The amount of entanglement any particular sub-system has, can be quantified in terms of its entanglement entropy, and therefore thought of as defining the area of a surface. So by breaking it down into all of its sub-systems and degrees of freedom, we can extract all of the 'surfaces' from any given wave function and potentially construct a geometry from pure entanglement.

If we consider the entanglement between two such 'surfaces', then where it is high they will have strong interactions, and where it is low their interactions will be weak. We can conceptualise the strength of these interactions as being representative of distance - Two surfaces that interact strongly are 'near' to each other, and two that interact weakly are 'far' apart.

Figure 3.27

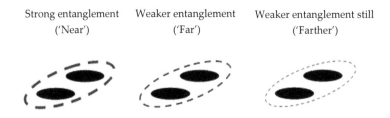

| Strong entanglement | Weaker entanglement | Weaker entanglement still |
| ('Near') | ('Far') | ('Farther') |

This is exciting not only because we can use it to construct a kind of geometry, but because of the fact that that geometry is based upon a relationship between entropy and area. Entropy tells us something about energy, and area is a geometric concept. Between them, energy and geometry form the two sides of Einstein's equations for gravitation, and in 1995 a physicist by the name of Ted Jacobson was actually able to **derive** General Relativity directly from the entropy of entanglement information alone…

He was able to show that as the quantum state changes, and the levels of entanglement change with it, the postulated emergent geometry changes and flexes in response. An increase in energy (perhaps due to the presence of a mass, for example) produces a reduction in entanglement (and therefore entropy), which shrinks the areas of the surfaces and causes the 'landscape' to curve.

And so out of pure entanglement information, we suddenly have a picture of a relativistic and dynamic space which warps and dilates in response to the presence of mass. Out of almost nothing, we have something resembling gravity… something resembling Spacetime.

Could this be how space arises from the underlying universal wave? Perhaps. In 2011, the Dutch physicist Erik Verlinde produced a paper suggesting that the majority of the information underlying the emergent geometry, lies in the entanglement between matter and another mysterious and 'dark' entity called 'dark energy'. Dark energy is an energy field of unknown origin which is driving the expansion of the universe. Einstein handled it by simply wrapping it up as a value he termed the 'cosmological constant'. It is required to make General Relativity work, and actually accounts for 70% of the content of the universe.

Most theories of gravity are based upon only the visible 5% of the universe, but entropic gravity incorporates it all (assuming if as it claims, dark matter doesn't really exist), which makes it attractive. So far though, the successes of the theory have been accompanied by significant setbacks, and it has received rather serious challenge from the physics community at large.

Thanks to the work of Jacobsen, it is quite widely accepted that there exists a thermodynamic interpretation of Einstein's equations, but whether or not Entropic Gravity in its current form represents the correct version of it is controversial. While it has been found to accurately predict the gravitational lensing around more than thirty three thousand galaxies, it is also known to get it wrong in the case of the Abell 1689 galaxy cluster. It is also inconsistent with observation in terms of the rotation velocities of dwarf galaxies, and is not yet applicable to the extreme conditions of black holes or the big bang/bounce at the 'birth' of the cosmos.

So while some results are hopeful, there is much work yet to be done. As a theory it remains highly speculative, but nonetheless represents an exciting avenue of enquiry which stands as another example of the potential held by entanglement, in teasing the classical spacetime background out of the purely quantum underlying state.

It is another hint that one way or another, quantum information (and its 'computation'), might well be amongst the most fundamental things to exist. More fundamental perhaps, than even space and time.

Time-like Entanglements

There is as yet, no consensus upon which of the varied approaches to quantum gravity will be the one which ultimately bears fruit. Perhaps it will even be something completely different to what has been considered so far - an approach that has not yet been conceived of. There is though, with the discovery of the remarkable notion that space can seemingly emerge as a by-product of entanglement, the growing acknowledgement that whatever the correct mechanism may be, entanglement is likely to hold the key.

In our deliberations so far though, we have only really considered the entanglement between things which exist 'at the same time'. That is to say, between things which are separated in space but share simultaneity in time.

Figure 3.28

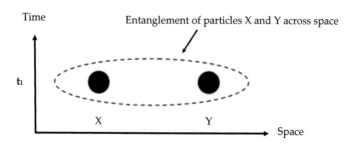

However, we know from Special Relativity that which things are simultaneous with each other is literally a matter of perspective. In figure

3.29, from the perspective of Alice the two particles are just entangled across space, yet they are entangled across both space **and** time from the perspective of Bob. He can see particle Y because it is intersected by his Now Slice, but its partner remains invisible to him because from his point of view, it lies in the future.

Figure 3.29

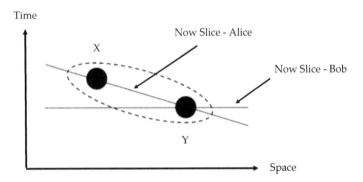

So entanglement is just as possible between things at different temporal locations, as it is between things at different spatial ones.

This entanglement across time can lead to some pretty unintuitive outcomes. Let's take a look for example, at what happens if we enhance the standard double slit experiment, such that it incorporates entanglement.

Figure 3.30 shows the standard setup with the addition of a crystal positioned just aft of the slits, and the detection screen offset at an angle.

Figure 3.30

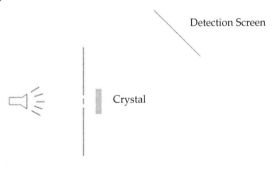

The crystal has the effect of 'splitting' the incoming photons into entangled pairs, which then continue on their way at an angle to each other as shown in figure 3.31.

Figure 3.31

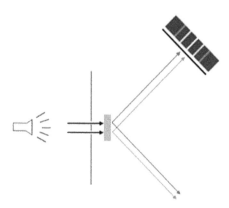

Regardless of their path through the slits, at the crystal each photon is transformed into an entangled pair, one of which ends up striking the detector screen, and one of which ends up missing it. The result at the screen is found to be an interference pattern, just as it would be in the standard version of the experiment (I.e. in the version without the crystal present). This is precisely what we might expect.

Now let's enhance the setup a bit further - let's introduce some detectors to measure the photons which miss the screen, as follows:

Figure 3.32

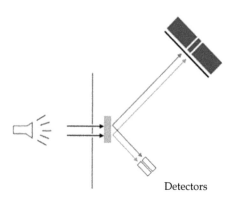

Detectors

The path to these newly introduced detectors is shorter than the path to the screen, and so the entangled photons reach them before their partners reach the screen. The result is that they entangle with the detectors, breaking their fungibility and decohering from their instances that exist in parallel histories. Because they are entangled with the photons that are heading towards the screen, those decohere too, and the outcome is that there is no interference pattern at the screen (as shown in figure 3.32).

So far, so good, and all is in line with what we have come to expect. However, something rather unintuitive happens if we tweak the experiment further, by moving the detectors such that the path to them is a greater distance than the path to the screen.

Figure 3.33

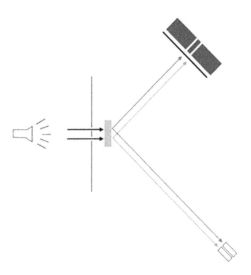

Now the photons arrive at our twin detectors later than their counterparts arrive at the screen. And the result? - Exactly the same as in the case of figure 3.32… we again see the pattern of two bright bands, even though the measurement at the detectors takes place **after** the photons strike the screen!

It is as though when the photons arrive at the screen, they 'know' that the ones they are entangled with are going to be measured in the future, and so behave accordingly. Another way of looking at it, might be to say that the future measurement *causes* the result in the past.

This is, of course, very reminiscent of the situation we found when we explored Lagrangian Mechanics in Part 1, and is simply a consequence of the fact that all of time exists all at once. The entangled pair constitute a single system which is required to be self-consistent across its full duration - even if one part of that system endures further into the future than the other.

As we have seen previously, there is no real distinction between the past, present, and future, and to divide time into those concepts is inherently false. All times exist on an equal footing, as per Einstein, and as per Wheeler -DeWitt. It is only our perception of it that is otherwise, and that perception is governed by our perspective.

Measuring the particles in the future didn't really 'change' the result that had already been recorded at the detection screen - it's simply that the 'future' was already there, and had already shaped the 'past' from the outset. Experiments of this nature are known as 'delayed choice' experiments, because they give the appearance of retro-causality, and expose the fact that all of time 'just is'.

What they also make clear, is the fundamental role that is played by entanglement.

In these examples though, we have so far only looked at the entanglement that exists across time between *multiple* things, but the fact that entanglement can span a temporal divide at all poses us an intriguing question - can a *single* object be entangled with *itself*, across time?

Figure 3.34

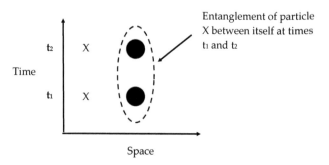

Entanglement of particle X between itself at times t_1 and t_2

In 2017, Martin Ringbaur and Rafael Chaves showed not only that it can, but in fact that it quite naturally **is.** In a paper that was motivated by the desire to lay the foundations for whether temporal correlations could be exploited for quantum information processing (such as quantum cryptography, for example), they used a technique called 'causal modelling' to show that temporal correlations do indeed exist between an object and the other instances of itself that are located at different times.

In the case of a single self-entangled object though, the manner in which the entanglement operates is a little different to the standard entanglement of two *different* things.

To see how, let's say that Bob and Alice are interested in the same particle, and are free to choose independently what properties they each measure. Let's also say that Bob makes his measurement at time t_1 and Alice takes hers at time t_2. The results they get are correlated with each other, but there is a key difference from the case of spatial entanglements. This is that Alice's measurement outcome is not dependent upon the outcome of Bob's, but is instead dependent upon the state that Bob's measurement left the particle in.

Figure 3.35

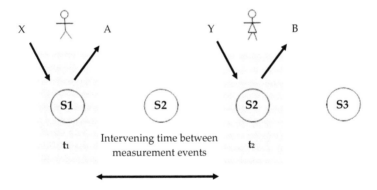

Bob measures property X at time t_1, obtaining result A. The process of his measurement though, changes the state of the particle from state S1 to state S2 (think Heisenberg's uncertainty principle). Alice then measures property Y at time t_2, obtaining result B. Her result is correlated with his, but this is due to the state that his measurement left the system in, rather than his result directly. This is important, because if we introduce further measurements, it has the consequence that the entanglement is only between states that are 'neighbouring'. I.e.

Figure 3.36

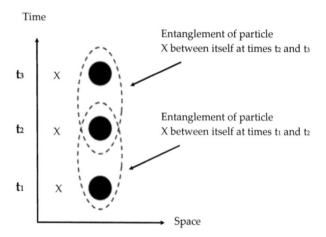

There is entanglement between the particle and itself at times t_1 and t_2, and between times t_2 and t_3, but importantly not directly between times t_1 and t_3. Any correlation that exists between those times, is mediated by the intervening state.

This might seem like a small detail, but it's crucial. It provides for us the final clue we need, in order to at last propose a solution to our perplexing puzzle of time's apparent flow. Because that solution will be based upon the framework of Wheeler and DeWitt, it should in principle remain independent of any particular approach to quantum gravity.

Of all the things we have learned, in the inherent composite nature of all things, the Everywhen harbours yet its most majestic of secrets...

" […] a single quantum system measured at different points in time exhibits Bell-like correlations"[17]

Martin Ringbauer & Rafael Chaves

Through the various strands of ongoing research into quantum gravity, a picture is slowly taking shape of the ways in which Spacetime might emerge from a fundamentally timeless world. The details are hazy, and exactly which model represents the correct path forwards is unclear, but at its base the world consists of a timeless and un-evolving quantum state.

It exists as a single quantum system that's in a superposition of all of its states, all at once. Those states are linked to one another by Quantum Mechanics, through which they are arranged into weakly interacting parallel histories, each manifesting as a full history of the classical and triumphantly emergent Spacetime block.

Figure 3.37

Individual histories of the classical Spacetime block

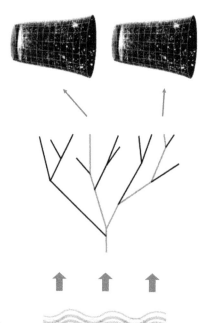

Web of parallel histories - 'The Multiverse'

Timeless quantum superposition

We have a good understanding of how the things of the world fall out of quantum fields and 'emerge', but we don't yet know the exact mechanism by which gravity (Spacetime itself) does. It may be through Quantum Geometrodynamics; it may be through Loop Quantum Gravity; the Holographic Principle; Entropic Gravity; or it may be through something entirely different. Nevertheless, we know that it **does** emerge, and some of the theories we have considered here offer some very bright sparks of hope that we will one day soon know the true mechanism for sure.

Whatever that mechanism is, it's looking increasingly likely that entanglement occupies centre-stage. We already know it to be responsible for the emergence of the history we perceive, and with the continued study of the nature of black holes, it's becoming more and more difficult to deny that it plays a similarly critical role in the construction of space itself. Perhaps this should not be surprising if we accept that just like everything else, the gravitational field is quantum mechanical - as is widely supposed.

In all of the miraculous things we have uncovered here in our pursuit of quantum gravity though, we have thus far found nothing that is not static. On the contrary, the vision of an eternal and unchanging reality without any flow, is only solidified and re-enforced.

However, with the discovery in recent years that entanglement happens not just across space within the same state, but also across sequentially ordered states that can be thought of as different 'times', new possibilities are opened-up.

With a tentative quantum mechanical framework for eternity (in the form of the Wheeler-DeWitt equation) to hand, and the magic of both spatial and temporal entanglement, we are now in a position where we can finally begin to conceive of how the internally perceived dynamics of the world could spring forth - of how the subjective perception of change might arise from the purely static and timeless, underlying quantum state.

We are ready to discover the rivers of time…

~

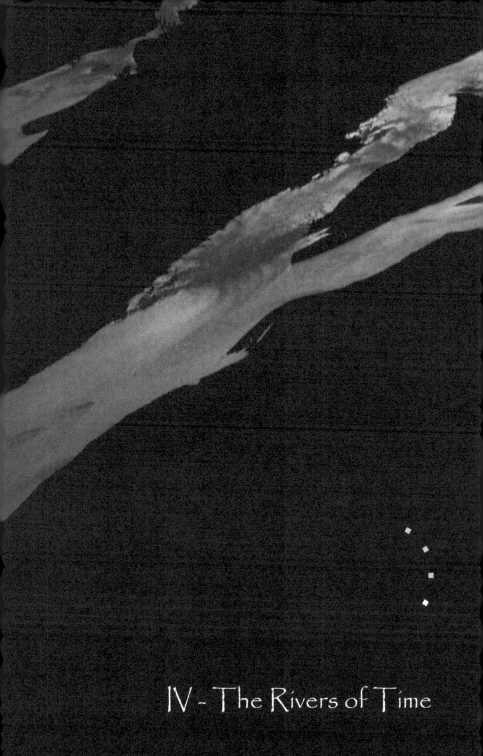

IV - The Rivers of Time

Behold,

The stillness keeps a secret,

Unto thyself shall be entwined,

The bowls in which to house the sacred,

- The minds with which,

To feel you move.

The Becoming

Bind to me,

For I am you...

Time does not exist at the fundamental level. It is simply not there. There are no time variables in the underlying laws of nature, but that does not, of course, mean it is not real.

There are no elephants in the fundamental laws of nature either. Nor any dolphins, rivers, lakes, or mountains, yet we are quite certain they exist.

The Standard Model of particle physics does not posit the existence of butterflies, diamonds, kisses, or love. It does not describe football matches, works of art, passion, lust, or poetry. It speaks nothing of our great cities, of travel, adventure, or the way the heart melts with the clasp of a child's hand around your finger. It says nothing of these things, and yet they, along with a great many other things that are not described at the fundamental level, are very real.

It says nothing of them because they are not basic elements of reality - they are emergent. They arise from the intricate interplay of trillions upon trillions of constituent parts, all locked into the beautiful dance which gives the things of this world their form; which creates an object to which we can point, and say 'that's an elephant'.

We are like this too. As is space, and as is time.

The very stage upon which the world plays out - the theatre in which we reside - is itself an emergent object. The Spacetime of Einstein and Minkowski is not an irreducible and passive background which acts as a simple container of things - it is a physical entity born of the very quantum interactions which give rise to its content. It **is** the things it contains, and the relations between them.

The exact mechanism by which Spacetime emerges from the underlying quantum reality is not yet known conclusively, though it seems increasingly clear that whatever that mechanism is, entanglement lies at the very heart of the mystery.

What we do know is that that Spacetime, in its eternal glory, is static. We know that nothing has ever moved within it, and that nothing ever will. We know that not only does all of time exist all at once, but that all possible histories do too, and that all of it - everything - the entire endless and infinite tree, is completely at rest. And yet we know that something, at least in some sense, must move.

As explored in Part 1, we are missing the magic ingredient that gives the world its subjective dynamism - its flow. How do we reconcile the way we know that the world must be, with the dynamical experience of living within it? How does the everyday process of change arise from something which is entirely changeless? And how do we account for human experience, and awareness?

We know that there has to be something more at play, because thought processes cannot be active in what are, by definition, entirely static snapshots - Thoughts ought to be frozen, just like everything else, and yet clearly, they are not. So if the missing element which allows for us to think, cannot be either a flow *of* time nor a flow *through* time, then it must be something else - some other mechanism - for else none of us has ever so much as had the privilege to conjure but a single thought.

So what exactly *is* the mysterious occurrence of flow, and where does it come from?

We have journeyed far in search of an answer, and in light of the things we have learned, and given that we know the universe to be quantum mechanical by nature, it would seem to make sense to begin by following

Everett, and considering it as a single quantum whole. That is, as a single quantum system.

The overall state of such a system is described by the magnificently timeless great equation of Wheeler and DeWitt. It is this picture of the world - one of an un-evolving overall quantum state - from which we begin. It is from this strange and mysterious realm in which time does not exist, that we must nevertheless recover the experience of its endless passage.

In spite of the seeming impossibility of the task, in 1983 the physicists Don Page and William Wootters succeeded in offering the tentative first steps towards answering this deepest of riddles. Their proposal, came to be known as the 'Page & Wootters Mechanism'. At its heart, once again lay the inscrutable magic of entanglement.

In echoes of Wheeler and DeWitt before them, they recognised that in the absence of time, the impression of a time evolution as experienced from the interior of the universe, can only be based upon some real physical variable (or combination of them) that is itself, also internal.

In other words, there must exist physical quantities inside the universe, which can somehow mimic the role of time. In order for them to successfully maintain the illusion that they **are** time, then to any observer located within the universe's interior, their effects should be indistinguishable from any notion of a genuine external time which they purport to simulate. Furthermore, they must achieve this without disrupting the overall static nature of the whole.

Undaunted by the scale of the challenge, their proposal was nothing short of genius...

In its un-evolving super-state, the universe exists perpetually in all of its states (across all of 'time'), all at once. That is to say, the underlying reality consists of an un-evolving superposition of all states - not just all states *at a given time*, but all states *at all times*.

That overall super-state though, can be decomposed into sub-systems. Let's take a photon to be one such sub-system, and say that each of its states are entangled with particular states of a second sub-system (which, for arguments sake, we could take to be the rest of the universe).

What we have then, is a superposition of entangled states:

Figure 4.1

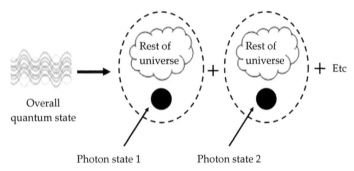

Overall
quantum state

Photon state 1   Photon state 2

The differing states of the photon, can be viewed as 'labelling' the states of the rest of the universe with which they are entangled. We could take its relative position, for example, to represent what 'time' it is within each entangled state. E.g.

Figure 4.2

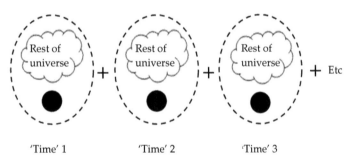

'Time' 1   'Time' 2   'Time' 3

So in this sense, we would have what is in effect, a superposition of 'moments' - all of which would be individually identifiable by the particular state of the photon, which to all intents and purposes, is serving as a clock. Note that all such 'moments' exist in the overall superposition simultaneously, just as they do in the classical picture.

The overall system has a correspondence with evolution over 'time', in the sense that the differing states of the 'clock' correspond to differing states of the rest of the universe. However, there is of course no genuine time-separation between each state - just a difference in the information content they embody.

Page and Wootters postulated that because of the entanglement, the effects of a measurement would be different for an observer located at an impossible position outside of the universe, than they would be for one on its interior. In fact they produced a mathematical proof demonstrating this difference, through quantum theory.

This showed that because the external observer would be performing their measurement upon the universe as a whole, they would find it to be a system displaying no division into different 'moments' at all, because they would be measuring the full composite (entangled) state overall.

Figure 4.3

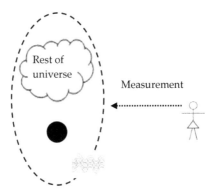

To the external observer, there are no distinct moments to be found in the universe, because from the outside perspective, they do not exist.

If on the other hand, the observer were positioned somewhere internal to the universe (as of course, they could only ever be), then they would necessarily find a very different situation - to them the division of the world into the 'moments' we have described, would be very real. They would, afterall, be viewing the world from within one of them. It is only from such intrinsic perspectives that distinct moments of time arise.

This is because from the inside perspective, observers do not have access to the whole, and as such can only ever measure sub-systems of it (because they are themselves a part of the system). Measuring sub-systems of the universal wave is just the bog-standard measurement process that we have been concerned with up until this point - an example of which is illustrated in Figure 4.4, where Alice is measuring a photon.

Figure 4.4

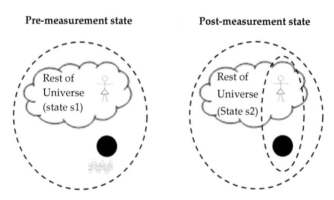

In the pre-measurement state, the photon is in a superposition, and Alice (who is a sub-system of the rest of the universe) has no entanglement with it directly. In the post-measurement state however, she is directly entangled with the photon and so finds it to be in a definitive state (because her measurement will have decohered one of its eigenstates from its superposition).

The differing states of the photon provide different 'labels' for the pre and post measurement states, and those two states appear to Alice to be different moments in time.

In terms of how the Schrödinger equation (which describes the dynamics of the system) works in the context of this internal perspective, the ideas of Wheeler and DeWitt are co-opted once again. As we are using the state of the photon in lieu of a time parameter, it is 'simply' a case of taking the same approach with regards to the equation – the state of the photon stands-in to play the role of the time parameter, and given that adjustment, Quantum Mechanics can be used in the standard manner to predict the probability amplitudes of the 'next' states.

So we can see that thanks to the miracle of entanglement, an entirely unchanging global state can give the appearance of distinct and ordered moments when viewed from within, without having to refer to any real time variable, and without compromising the integrity of its overall static nature.

This however, should not be confused with the emergence of flow. There is still no actual transition between states here - just the effective and self-consistent division of the world into different 'times', which manifest to the internal observer in a way in which they do not to the external one.

It is nevertheless a remarkable leap, and provides the previously absent grounding for why there are dual descriptions of the universe - one that describes a timeless overall whole, and one that describes interacting sub-systems possessing evolution over time.

It was to be thirty two years that were to pass between the proposal of the Page & Wootters Mechanism, and its experimental verification.

In 2015, a group led by Ekaterina Moreva at the Istituto Nazionale di Ricerca Metrologica (INRIM) in Turin, performed a test of the idea using a 'toy universe' consisting of a pair of entangled photons, and an observer. Their experiment had two setups, both of which involved altering the polarization of the photons by passing them through a quartz plate.

In the first setup - designed to simulate the experience of an observer internal to the universe - the observer measures the polarisation of one photon, and then compares it with the polarisation of the second. Here, the measured photon is playing the role of the clock, while the other is playing the role of the rest of the universe. A difference in the polarisations confirms the Page & Wootters 'internal' picture of 'time labelled' states (with the state of the measured photon providing the 'label' for the other).

In the second setup - designed to simulate the experience of an observer external to the universe - the observer measures the global properties of both photons by comparing them against an independent clock. Here, the 'external' Page & Wootters scenario is confirmed by an absence of any discernible change to the global (composite) state.

In both setups, the experiment confirmed beautifully Page & Wootters' intuition, and showed that 'temporal' separation of states can be viewed as an emergent phenomenon which occurs as a by-product of entanglement.

Elegant as this mechanism is though, there are a couple of issues which prevent it (in the form presented thus far) from being a truly representative picture of reality. It should instead be thought of as a kind of proof-of-concept - a prototype for the sort of mechanism that could, in principle, be at play in coaxing time out of the timeless. It provides for us a blueprint upon which refinements can be built.

The issues are namely:

1) The choice of clock is arbitrary - there are many such sub-systems that could be decomposed from the quantum state and chosen to serve as a 'clock', and there is no reason to think they would all be in agreement. This problem is referred to as 'clock ambiguity'.

2) As already stated, there is still no *flow* of time in this model. We have a sort of time-labelling of states; there is an absence of change to the global state; and we have predictions about what the next states would be when viewed from any given internal perspective, but there is still nothing to actually transition the world to those next states. It is still completely stationary, even as viewed from the internal perspective.

David Deutsch picked up the baton in 1990, and updated the model in a number of ways. One was to include a more realistic measurement process - one which occurs over the course of a number of states, rather than the idealised single state as presented in the Page and Wootters example. Another, importantly, was to identify the clock with the rest of the universe, rather than with the particle undergoing measurement.

Figure 4.5

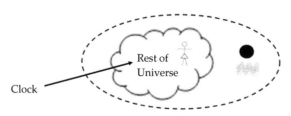

Looking at it this way around has the great advantage that it immediately removes problem 1) outlined above. The choice of clock is no longer arbitrary - there is only one that it can be, and that is the full state of the rest of the universe.

This chimes with what we have discussed previously in 'The Identity of a Moment', where we concluded that a moment is simply defined by the things it contains, and is 'timestamped' ('labelled') by that content.

Deutsch also made it more explicit that post-measurement, there is not a *single* 'next' state that is selected for, but rather a whole set of them (the set corresponding to the ensuing Everett branches of the wave function that result from the measurement). In other words, there are 'next' states in many parallel timelines, as opposed to just one.

Figure 4.6

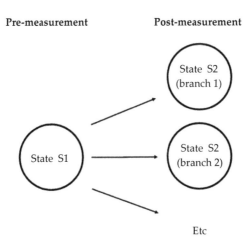

He also took the view that each state can effectively be thought of as its own 'world', so to speak.

'The division of the world into "instants of time" is just a special case of its division into Everett branches'[18]

David Deutsch

While these are significant improvements on the model, they still leave issue 2) unresolved - there is still no actual transition between states. There is still no 'flow' of time.

Picking up on this point in 2018, the theorists Bryan and Medved appealed to the 'psychological arrow of time' to build upon the picture further. This is the observation that memories are encoded into the state of the observer at each of their 'moments', providing for them a record of states and events that have occurred in 'the past'. As has been discussed in 'The Arrow of Time & the Problem of Flow' though, this only provides a partial resolution (as also acknowledged by Bryan and Medved) in that it accounts for why an observer in any given state would have the impression that they had lived the moments leading up their 'present' (assuming electrical signals could actually flow in their brains and allow them to think those kind of thoughts in the first place - which in reality they could not).

All physical objects in fact make records (or 'memories') of one form or another, as they are altered by the interactions they have had. The resulting altered state is in itself a form of record of the interaction, providing a reference to the things which have happened 'in the past'. The making of records inevitably incurs heat emission, and hence an unavoidable rise in entropy in successive states. So the thermodynamic and psychological arrows of time both quite naturally always point in the same direction due to the natural correspondence between the making of records, and its associated increase of entropy.

So we now have a quantum mechanical picture that corresponds very well (the inclusion of gravity aside) to the classical world of Einstein and Minkowski, which generated the mystery of time for us in the first place. We have an overall state that is static and includes all moments across all of time; We have an 'inside' perspective of distinct definitive moments which are 'time-stamped' by the configuration of the universe in that particular instant; we have the observer's impression of having lived through a past; and we have the thermodynamic and psychological arrows of time both pointing in the same direction.

But even with this enhanced Page & Wootters setup in place, our problem is not resolved. We still have no description of how the observer at S1 feels as though she 'becomes' the one at S2. There is still nothing to account for the impression of a transition from one state to the next.

Figure 4.7

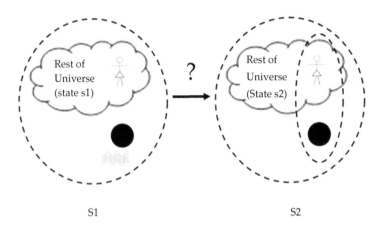

Why should the S1 Alice feel as though she 'becomes' the S2 Alice, when we in fact know them to exist concurrently? Why should she, as we all certainly do, have the *experience* of that motion through time?

Thanks to the work of Ringbaur and Chaves, we know that the model outlined thus far is incomplete, because there must also be time-like entanglements present too. A system which is present in any two temporally 'neighbouring' states, is naturally entangled with *itself* across those states.

Figure 4.8

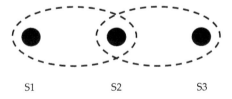

It is these 'temporal' correlations between the time-like separations of state which, I propose, complete the picture for us.

As we well know, the constituent parts of entangled systems cannot be properly described independently of each other. There is rather a global state that is spread across them. It is inseparable from them.

This poses an intriguing question, for in the case of a single object that has the necessary structure for awareness (such as a person, for example) being entangled with itself across states (across 'time'), one is moved to ask what it might be like to be at both ends of the overall system at once - what it is like to be the composite.

In her entangled state, Alice is neither her state at S1 nor her state at S2 individually - she is both of them **simultaneously**. This is shown in figure 4.9, where I'm showing her entanglement with herself, and with the rest of the universe (the 'clock').

Figure 4.9

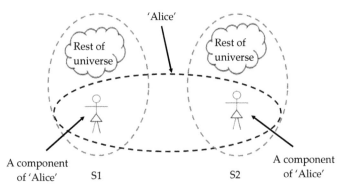

She is not actually two systems at different temporal locations after all, but instead exists as a single composite system spanning both. She has physicality at both S1 and S2 simultaneously. There are differences between the precise configurations of the particles that constitute her brains in each of those states, and so there is an information delta between them. Her two physical minds are in ever-so-slightly different states. They are each in a configuration of their memory, plus information that is incoming from the state of the world with which they are entangled. Given that she is a composite of both of those minds at once, could the difference between them be what she experiences as change?

If she is able to perceive the world at both S1 and S2 simultaneously, then certainly the state of the world at S2 will appear to have moved by way of comparison to its state at S1. But **can** she perceive that change?

The mechanism by which conscious awareness emerges is not understood, but what we can say is that the position of the electrons in her brain will have shifted ever-so-slightly between the two states. A neuron that was not firing at S1, for example, may be in the early stages of beginning to fire at S2. So the differences in the brain between the two states can be summarised as the movement of electrical signals, and it this which (somehow) gives rise to awareness; to thought. Conscious awareness though, occurs over time-spans of the order of a second - much larger than the gap between the immediately neighbouring states in our example (which I am taking to have a measure of one Planck Time), so the degree of change between the states in unlikely to be sufficient to amount to an awareness.

Note however, that just as S1 is temporally entangled with S2, so S2 is temporally entangled with S3. Hence if we know her to be a composite of both S1 and S2, then it follows that she is in fact also a composite of S2 and S3, as depicted in figure 4.10.

Figure 4.10

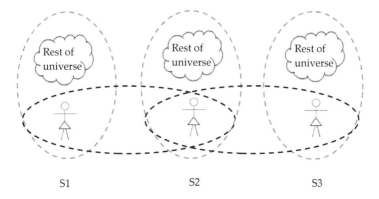

So Alice exists across all three states simultaneously. If we take the case of her S2 component, we can see that it actually forms a part of two different instances of 'Alice' - one that straddles an interval I1 between state S1 and S2, and one that straddles an interval I2 between states S2 and S3.

Figure 4.11

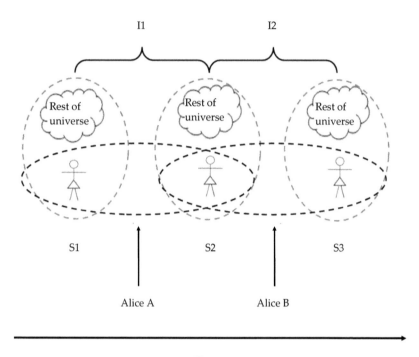

'Time'

Those 'Alice instances' overlap through state S2. For Alice A, S2 (or rather the difference between it and S1) is responsible for the feeling that she is 'moving from' S1, and for Alice B, S2 (or rather the difference between it and S3) is responsible for the feeling she is 'moving to' S3. In this way, S2 serves as a 'link' which ties Alices A and B together into a 'chain'.

As discussed in part 3, due to the nature of time-like entanglements, the difference between S1 and S3 is not accessed directly, but via the intermediary state, S2. As such, although she can be thought of as having continuity from S1 to S3, her experience is of successive change across the two intervals, I1 and I2.

It doesn't take much reasoning to realise that this type of chaining happens across **all** states of Alice, along the full duration of her world-line.

Figure 4.12

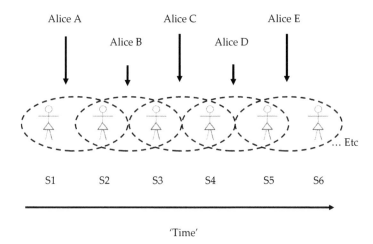

'Time'

This makes for a smooth and continuous experience of sequential change across successive intervals. Knowing that consciousness happens at the scale of roughly one second, we can work backwards and infer that it takes the gauging of change across approximately 5.39×10^{44} such intervals (the number of Planck Times in one second), for that change to have typically included enough of a differential in the neural pathways of her brain, to amount to a conscious experience - for her to become aware.

From her perspective, the circumstance of the world across those 5.39×10^{44} states, has changed. This leaves her with the impression of living in a dynamically changing environment, in which time has the appearance of sweeping her forwards through the world along its never-ending 'flow'. To her, the illusion of time's passage is every bit as real as the world itself, for it is here, in the entanglement of ourselves across temporal states, that time's mighty river truly lies.

In the composite nature of all things, we have finally discovered an answer to the great mystery we set out to resolve, but that is not all we have found. Indeed, through its mechanism, we have found something that is as magical as it is unexpected - we have found something about ourselves.

Due to our entanglement, our questions regarding identity from 'The Eternals' chapter of Part 1, have a resolution too. There, we were concerned with whether or not the many instances of Bob located at different points in time, could in fact be justified as being thought of as a single 'joined-up' entity.

Figure 4.13

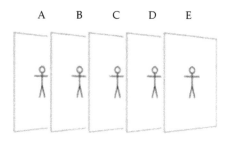

Thanks to the phenomenon of temporal entanglement, they can, but the truth is more subtle than we could have imagined. There is no single physical instance of Bob which fully accounts for him at any given point. Instead, those physical instances are more akin to 'book-ends' between which he exists. They are physical states which bound him. Through his self-entanglement, between any given sequential states he is both 'book-ends' at once, and the *experience* of being Bob is the information gap which lies between them. He is the delta between states, which chain to form a single continuous entity distributed across time.

Figure 4.14

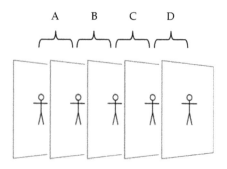

There are four instances of Bob in figure 4.14 - not the five we assumed in figure 4.13. They are A, B, C, and D, and they exist in a state of singular continuity. The description can also be extended to bring branching into the picture, and to account for the versions of ourselves that exist in different histories too.

For the sake of simplicity of the diagram, in figure 4.15 I'm showing only Alice and her temporal entanglements. All other entanglements with the world are assumed, rather than explicitly depicted. She is shown as the composite states which straddle her individual states, and is labelled with the letters A to F.

Figure 4.15

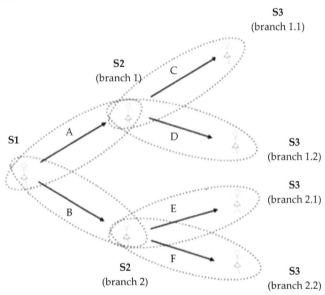

We can see that following a branching event, all subsequent Alice's can trace their histories back through their conscious experience to the same point.

The sequence AC represents a single history, as do AD, BE and BF. Thanks to the psychological arrow of time, each Alice will have memories of 'being' those Alice's to the 'left' of them in the same history, while remaining blissfully unaware of those which lie either to the 'right', or in parallel histories. Alice C has continuity from Alice A, for example, and can 'remember' her, but is completely unaware of Alice's D, B, E, and F. This of course, is in line with our actual experience.

But just because our physical instances do in the end, constitute the many components of a joined-up entity, that does not mean to say that we each have only a single awareness. If we zoom out and look at any particular branch 5.39×10^{44} states at a time, we can see that there are conscious experiences happening all the way along it simultaneously.

Figure 4.16

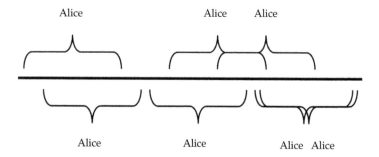

Alice   Alice   Alice

Alice   Alice   Alice   Alice

(A section of a single history of Alice, illustrating a random selection of her many overlapping awareness's, which perpetually exist simultaneous with each other)

Between any chosen human states separated by approximately 5.39×10^{44} intervals, there is a conscious experience in the process of happening.

There are many, many versions of each of us existing simultaneously in any given history - all busy having a conscious experience. They overlap, and for each person, there is one beginning at every Planck Time for which they have a boundary state. None of them are 'stuck' against the immovable wall of a particular Now - they merge into one another, and thanks to their entanglement, have the impression of being moved through their moments like leaves being swept downriver on the current.

But that is not to say they are helpless passengers - they helped shape those rivers through the choices they've made, both in the past, and in the future. They are choices made timelessly through a process of top-down feedback between themselves and the fundamental reality from which they emerge.

The miracle of our awareness lies not in our *being*, but in the relentless events of our constant *becoming*. We, and by that I mean the sentient thought processes which constitute the 'I' that is at the heart of each of us, are not to be found within the *things* of this world. We are instead the product of the *differentials* between the states of those things. We are the product of change. We *are* change. We are the process. We are what resides in the gaps between states, anchored in the world by the physical vessels of our bodies, which in their myriad static instances, are but a vast succession of boundary points of change from which we arise, emergent.

The sublime existence of awareness, is not achieved from within the narrow confines of any one static Now. We are not any particular single instance of ourselves - we are **all** of them, many at a time, and conscious experience, intangible and immaculate, is the cumulative experience of that perpetual *becoming* with which we straddle our physical states.

In any interval between given points, we gauge the amount of change we traverse relative to the things with which we are entangled, and we give that quantity a label. We call it 'the passage of time'.

Amid the endless branches of the infinite tree, we are like skaters on a frozen sea, following the paths of secret currents of time which snake through the Spacetime block like hidden rivers, as each of us in our multitude, glides merrily across a motionless blur of static worlds unending.

At the book-ends of being,

You'll find me at rest,

As the manifest frames,

Which you took me to be,

From the gap between worlds,

I'll smile dear brightly,

I was never those things,

But the space in-between.

Vanquished shadows flee clear eyes,
Nature in its truthful guise,
Infinitely sprawling deep and vast,
That which flows revealed as still,
Kings correlation and free will,
Endless echoed futures shape the past.

Decohering system branches,
Render realms unto each path,
Emergent conscious thought observing,
O'er that in which its basis hath,
The tree bears fruit in human knowledge,
Decorating paths unfurled,
Choices made so sculpt creation,
As unbeknownst we slip 'cross worlds...

II

III

IV

V

V – The Magnificence

Bewitched by the motion,

Entranced by its splendour,

Eternity moving,

In stillness profound,

All worlds to abide,

The wave everlasting,

Mesmeric the cradle,

Of life to behold.

The Totality of Being

The study of time has shown it to be at once malleable and subjective, and yet all the while entirely fixed and unchanging. That duality which lies at the heart of all things, rendering them static, immutable, and timeless; yet dynamic, shifting, and ephemeral, is one of the most deeply profound and mesmerizing features of what is a truly remarkable world - a world which flows without flowing; passes without passing; and through which we travel without moving.

We are necessarily a part of that world. We are not simply living within it as though it is some sort of arena that is independent of us. We are constructed of it. Everything in the Multiverse is made of the same quantum fields. Fluctuations in those fields form emergent patterns, and one such pattern manifests as a plain of wild grasses over there, while others manifest as you and I over here.

The answer to the question of 'what am I?' is much more complex and subtle than we ever imagined. Not only does it reside somewhere within the mysterious inner-workings of the mind, but is also embedded deeply in the nature of time.

Without a flow of time we would simply be inanimate objects with the requisite structure for awareness, whose potential would remain unrealised. It is that all-important and magical 'flow' which completes us. It joins us together into coherent wholes, and I believe is generated through the entanglement of entirely static, but ever-so-slightly different instances of ourselves at different 'moments'.

Of all the great revelations we have encountered, it is that idea that any one physical embodiment of us is but a single part - an individual component - of what we really are, that is to me perhaps the most incredible. Take a snapshot of any one of us at any given moment, and at best all you have captured is half a person. You've snapped just one side of a double-headed coin, and mistaken it for the whole. The rest of it is residing enigmatically at other moments, while our quintessence hides ethereally in the difference between them.

The immeasurable beauty of this is amplified and compounded by the notion that we each have not one, but a great many awareness's which are perpetually in transition, like trains moving along the inanimate 'tracks' of our static states, constituting the immense multitude of people throughout history that we could rightly choose to term 'I'. Those tracks of course, fork with every interaction, exploding that plethora of people into an incomprehensible number across the multiverse in its totality.

The manner in which we choose to think of ourselves, hence depends greatly upon the definition of 'I' that we each happen to prefer, and what exactly it is that we mean by it. If for example, you limit it to meaning the conscious experience you are having in whatever you take to be the present moment, then we can say that for you, 'I' refers to a single train of awareness moving along the track of a single branch of the multiverse. In this case though, should all the other trains on that same branch be thought of as other people, even though they arise from the same chain of static states as 'you', and even though they share each and every one of your thoughts, emotions, and experiences?

Figure 5.1

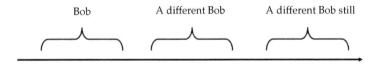

If instead by 'I' you include your history as well as your experience of the present moment, then you are simultaneously every train on that track up until that point, even though they are all alive and busy having individual experiences. In this case would it not make more sense to talk of 'we' instead of 'I'?

Figure 5.2

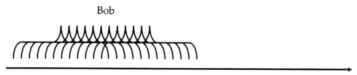

And what of those that are positioned to the future? They are experiencing too... Are you not those ones as well?

Perhaps 'you' are an entire branch then? In that case, 'I' refers to **all** of the awareness's that arise from your static states within a single history.

Figure 5.3

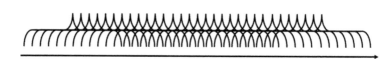

And if we are happy to go this far, then is it not also logical to extend this line of thinking across histories?

Figure 5.4

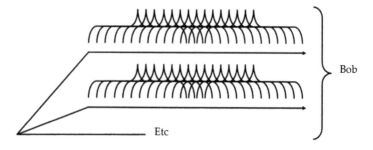

Part of the difficulty we have here, I suspect lies in the use of language and terminology - our vocabulary has simply not evolved in the context of these questions. Perhaps we would be best served to address this and define some sort of delineation in our meaning when it comes to the issue of what we are trying to convey when we say 'I'.

We could, for instance, choose to single out the examples I have used here, and label them as I-SubjectivePresent, I-SubjectiveHistoric, I-SubjectiveBranch, and I-ObjectiveWhole, respectively. Such descriptions are of course just arbitrary, and miss entirely the vast majority of the equally valid categorisations that we could choose, but they perhaps capture the ones that somehow feel the most natural.

In previous pages I have promoted the view that the parallel versions of us are different people. This is a philosophical standpoint. It is a way of speaking, and a manner of thinking.

I choose the viewpoint that I do, because it is the one which allows me to personally make the most sense of my life. I prefer to think of 'I' as the one which is I-SubjectiveBranch, but that is not to say it is the only view one could take.

Who is to really say which manner of thinking is the most appropriate? Who is to say that one way of mapping the 'I' of our everyday language onto any one of these definitions is any more correct than another?

Figure 5.5

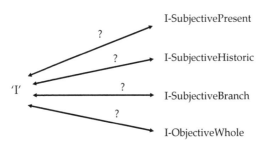

Perhaps in the end, the most rational thing we can say is that it's a matter of personal taste. If you choose to define yourself as being only one of your trains (I-SubjectivePresent), then you are correct from a certain point of view. If you go to the other extreme and choose to define yourself as being all of your trains on all of your tracks across all histories (I-ObjectiveWhole), then you are also correct - just from a different point of view.

The cause of the difficulty in assigning a single definitive mapping here, is that teasing apart the conundrum of how many of the instances of ourselves we can sensibly claim to be 'us', is like attempting to answer the question of how many experiences we had yesterday. The boundaries of experience are not clearly cut and sharply defined - they merge into one another, blending, fusing, and blurring, and they can be defined at many different levels of abstraction. You could argue, for instance, that yesterday was one continuous experience for you, just as you could argue with equal validity that it was a collection of any arbitrary number of them.

In the same way, we can select any states that bound us, and rightly claim to be whatever lies between. The choice of boundaries is arbitrary, because any given state is entangled with another, and much like experiences, they blend into one another.

The problem of the arbitrary selection of boundaries in fact extends beyond the question of which awareness's we think of as being 'us', and into a much broader arena of discussion. This is because it is not just between the different instances of ourselves that it is problematic to draw a proper and meaningful separation, but also between us and those things which we would typically think of as being other objects - as things which are outside of our selves.

This is the question of exactly what it is that defines where our bodies begin and where they end. When you get down to the atomic scale, precisely which atoms should be considered a part of us, and which should not? Traditionally, we might take the view that it is whether or not an atom is chemically bound to us that determines whether or not it is a part of our body, but that is to generalise and over-simplify.

Consider the case of a blood cell, for instance. It is not bound to the rest of the body - it is something which is moved through it. So should the atoms from which it is made be considered a part of the body or not? They are manufactured by the body, and are important to our survival, so I suspect most of us would feel that they probably should, but this is just a point of view. What if that blood cell were to leave the body - would it still be considered to be a part of it if it were spilled? For most practical intents and purposes, it is probably no longer useful to think of it in that way, although a forensic pathologist may disagree.

And what of things such as gut bacteria, with which we share a symbiosis?

The point is that on these, and on a great many other points besides, you can make rational arguments either way. It very quickly becomes less of a matter of fact, and more a matter of opinion and perspective. The difficulties arise quite readily, and that is in spite of the fact that we have so far restricted the argument to only issues of the classical world. What if we were to talk about actual reality, and ask what it does to our answers when entanglement is introduced to the picture?

What of the air that we breathe, or the sunlight that warms us? They would not ordinarily be considered a part of us, and yet whether it be an atom of oxygen, or a photon of light, if it has an interaction with us then we become part of a composite system with it.

We are in fact entangled with anything with which we have any interaction at all, and from a quantum perspective, have to view them as being parts of the same system as ourselves. So the question of quite where the boundaries which delineate our static states from the rest of the world lie (or even to what extent it makes sense to consider such boundaries to exist), is an awkward one.

As human beings, we like to categorise and label things - to 'put them in boxes', so to speak. But nature cares little for our quaint preferences. The natural world just simply is, and is completely indifferent to our colloquial urge to manufacture categorisations that we can impose, in order that we might be better able to conceive of it, or of ourselves.

The classical world is an emergent phenomenon which is born of the quantum. It is a zoomed-out approximation of the underlying reality, and can be defined at any given level of abstraction. Which particular level makes sense to us, or happens to be useful to our understanding, makes no difference to the underlying truth.

Quantum Mechanics cares not whether you're an atom or a collection of them. It makes no distinction as to whether you're the broken vial, or the cat. It applies equally and indifferently to all things, and operates upon the world as though it were a single unified quantum system.

Everything in the universe is governed and described by the one and the same Universal wave function, and ultimately, we cannot rightly be regarded as separate from it. Just like experiences, we can approximate boundaries between ourselves and other objects within that wave to whatever degree of abstraction that we feel makes sense to us, but in the end, because of our entanglement with the world, there is no truly independent way of describing us without also describing it.

There is only an arbitrary distinction in that respect, between us, the grasses, the rock, the clouds, the sky, the stars, and the galaxies, for we are but different aspects and expressions of the same fundamental quantum reality. We do not have separate wave functions, but are more exactly different entangled sub-systems of the same overall thing - the strange and remarkable thing we call creation.

From an entirely holistic perspective, in our completeness, we are capriciously defined parts of a much wider whole - a whole which includes everything that exists - from the dessert winds and the mountain rains, to the fiery depths of the sun; the ice fountains of Enceladus; and the farthest-flung reaches of the universe.

We are a living, breathing, section of the world, which in our constant becoming, is not only aware but self-aware - free to debate philosophical questions of boundaries and self, and to bear witness to the flows, rhythms, and cycles of the ever-present and eternal process of change in the changeless... a process which is a feature of the world reflected deeply in the nature of all things.

In its splendour and glory, that process conjures tangible and dynamic classical realms from the profound stillness of the totality of being.

It is a process called 'Time'.

On hallowed ground the temple bell,

Calls softly through the dawn,

The stir of echoes wakes the day,

And holds it up reborn.

The daily cycle of the Earth,

- The halves that make the whole,

Is mirrored always in thyself,

- A portrait of the soul.

Forever in motion,

The world keeps on turning,

Like me.

With the last of the light,

The day turns to night,

Like me.

At the break of the dawn,

A new day is born,

Like me.

Reflections

What is time?

More than three decades have passed since I sat in the back of the family car and first asked myself that question. Yet in spite of time's passage, I am still marvelling at its mystery - not only from my current present as an adult, but also from the past, as quite literally the same boy, sat in the same car, full of questions and wonder.

That boy exists there permanently, forever etched into the fabric of the world at those particular Now Slices, and is 'right now' living out the magical experience that I described in the preface. He's feeling the warmth of the sun's rays on his face; he's hearing the sounds of the radio; and he's staring transfixed upon the movement of the hands on his wristwatch.

I believe now that he is not any one particular physical instance of himself, but is instead the product of the differentials between his static states - states that we interpret as being different 'times'. He exists across his physical instances, and traverses them without anything of which he is made ever moving.

I believe that the miracle of subjective dynamism - the experience that we call the 'flow of time' - has its roots in the quantum mechanical wonders of superposition, entanglement, and decoherence, and that between them they generate not only time's perceived flow, but the plethora of alternate histories that are realised across the world in its fullness - not as possibilities, or potentialities, but as physical realities every bit as solid as the ones which we know.

Through our free-will we help to shape that intricately woven web of alternate histories through the choices we make, and I know that even though it is us who makes them, they are choices we have 'already' made in what from our current perspective is the 'future'. We know that those future choices exert an influence over the past, and that our moments are but particular arrangements within the universal superposition, as viewed from a certain perspective. Those precious moments persist forever, carved into the very structure of time, indelible and fixed.

Although I know these things to be true, knowing something on an intellectual level, and really *knowing* it deeply and intuitively are two very different things. It is the difference between knowing the sequence and timing of keys to be struck, and really *knowing* how to make a piano sing. It is the difference between having a theoretical understanding of the feeling of love, and *knowing* it first hand. It is the difference between knowing that time is not what it seems, and really *knowing* it at a deep and instinctive level.

Every now and then - in fleeting moments of clarity - I swear I can taste its essence, but like the flicker of starlight, with a blink it is gone - dwarfed and consumed by the overwhelming force of what Einstein called the 'stubbornly persistent illusion' of our everyday experience. For the most part, it exists as a feeling hiding somewhere just beyond the rim of memory - like the words you search for on the tip of your tongue, or the visions you try to recall as you stir slowly from the embers of a dream.

Yet in silent moments, I can close my eyes and recognise in myself a deep and moving affinity for those past versions of myself, whom I know to be living-out all the joys and sorrows of which I have had a first-hand experience. I wonder about how things have unfolded for them in parallel worlds, where their circumstance, choices, and outcomes were different. I wonder too about what the future holds, and which branch of it this particular version of me will come to know.

The human quest for knowledge, far from stripping the world of its mystery, in the end only ever seems to deepen it. The further we go, the more magical we find it to be, and as one question is answered so too others are brought more sharply into focus. The proposal that the experience of time's flow has its roots in entanglement between different static instances of ourselves, really only addresses half of the question, for the ability to experience and reflect upon reality in the first place is a privilege reserved only for the sentient - for the conscious. Precisely what that consciousness is, is surely one of the next great mysteries waiting to be solved, and who knows what wonders lie awaiting our discovery there?

We have explored here a potential explanation for why thought processes are not frozen in the static states of matter from which they arise, but the simple fact that a piece of the universe - a creature such as a person, which is at its base nothing more than an ordered and structured collection of atoms - can be arranged in such a way as to achieve a state of self-awareness is, quite frankly, utterly astounding. How does it happen? What is it about the structure of the brain that facilitates it? And what exactly, is *it* anyway?

To my mind, there is a large part of the riddle of how we are able to perceive the passage of time that remains shrouded in the cloak of the unknown, and that part is us. It is what is termed as 'the hard question' of neuroscience.

Another very hard question is how the world (the multiverse) came to be instantiated. As we have seen, time is something which is intrinsic to it, and as such it has no beginning and it has no end - it just has boundary conditions. It is outside of time. In the absence of a time that is external to it, it therefore cannot have a cause. It is timeless and eternal, and can only be self-consistent across its bulk. How does something like that come into being? How did the timeless quantum superposition that underlies the multiverse come to be? (Note that I can't even seem to articulate the question without falsely reverting to the use of temporal tenses and language).

It is the ultimate question, and perhaps someday the study of quantum gravity will furnish us with an answer, or perhaps it will remain tantalisingly ever beyond our reach. For now at least, we are forced to acknowledge that the answer is not just unknown, but potentially unknowable.

What we do know is that the things of the world persist in perpetuity, and are not isolated but inter-connected, forming the rich tapestry of space, time, and histories through which we relate. Space is the emergent concept of locality which is defined by the manner in which things are entangled, and time is the measure of the differences in state between them.

The boy in the car will live forever. Ahead of him lie an incomprehensible number of futures, and he will grow up to live them all. In some of those futures he will uncover answers to his questions, and will go on to attempt to convey a sense of their majesty in these pages. Within that set of timelines in which he does, there is a further subset in which you will find yourself reading what he's committed into print, and somewhere within **that** group, is the history you're experiencing now.

I hope sincerely that you find it to be a good one, and that your experience of it is perhaps in some way enriched by a deeper understanding of the true way of time, and of the incredible nature of the reality it demands. I hope too that those understandings manage to move you in something akin to the manner in which they move me, and that they conspire to make a contribution towards your appreciation for the unparalleled magnificence of the world in which we live.

Amid all the beauty of that world, I believe whole-heartedly that the most precious thing it contains is sentient thought, and that of all thoughts, the one's which are most exquisite, are those of wonder, awe, mystery, and love.

They are mine, and they are yours. They are the precious gifts of a life indebted to something which at the fundamental level, doesn't even exist - an all-pervading something called 'Time'.

All love and all dreams,

All darkest desires,

All cruelty and torment,

All beacons of hope,

All childhood sweet laughter,

All triumphs and glory,

All truth in its fullness,

In Time ever bound.

We are the ethereal,

\- The ghosts in the machine,

Making animate the stationary,

Through the bridging of thought,

Eternal tenants,

To immeasurable Nows,

In awe of their beauty,

Enthralled by their way.

This burning sun,

These morning skies,

Full life in its glory,

For you love,

And I.

Glossary of Terms

2nd Law of Thermodynamics
Physical law stating that the entropy of a closed system will always increase over time.

Action
An attribute of the dynamics of a physical system, having dimensions of energy and time. Calculated as the result of a mathematical function which takes the trajectory of the system as its input, and integrates the difference between its kinetic and potential energies at every point along the trajectory.

Anti-De Sitter Space
A category of shape of the universe, which has a negative cosmological constant, and negative curvature.

Arrow of Time
The consistent direction of forwards evolution through the temporal dimension.

Atom
The smallest component of an element having the chemical properties of the element. It consists of a nucleus containing combinations of neutrons and protons with one or more electrons bound to it by electrical attraction; the number of protons determines the identity of the element.

Bell Inequality
Mathematical construct which demonstrates that, assuming quantum entities do not obtain specific values for their observables until a measurement of those observables is made, then no theory which seeks to retain the principles of realism and locality can make the same predictions as quantum mechanics.

Big Bang
The postulated faster-than-light sudden expansion of Spacetime, which is thought to have occurred almost immediately after the initial boundary condition of the universe.

Big Bounce
A hypothetical cosmological model, in which the first cosmological event in the universe was the result of the collapse of a previous universe.

Black Hole
A region of Spacetime where the gravitational field is so intense that no matter or radiation can escape.

Block Universe
See Spacetime block.

BOOMERanG
Balloon Observations Of Millimetric Extragalactic Radiation And Geophysics.

Born Rule
A key postulate of quantum mechanics, which gives the probability that a measurement of a quantum system will yield a given result.

Branching
The process by which parallel histories are created as a result of the natural evolution of the wave function according to the Many Worlds interpretation of quantum mechanics.

Brownian Motion
The erratic random movement of microscopic particles suspended in a fluid, as a result of continuous bombardment from molecules of the surrounding medium. It was the topic of one of Einstein's three great papers of 1905, and was pivotal in the acceptance of the existence of atoms.

Causal Models - Mathematical models representing causal relations within a system or population.

Causality
The relationship between cause and effect. Also referred to as 'causation'.

Classical Physics
Non-quantum physics.

Consciousness
The awareness of your unique thoughts, memories, feelings, sensations, and environment.

Copenhagen Interpretation
A reading of quantum mechanics in which quantum entities do not posses any physically realised properties until they undergo observation.

De Broglie Wave
The wave-like characterisation of matter.

De Sitter Space
A category of shape of the universe, which has a positive cosmological constant, with either a positive or flat curvature. Includes Minkowski space.

Decoherence
The process by which the information of a quantum sub-system is altered by its interaction with its environment, creating an entanglement between the environment and itself, and thereby breaking its coherence with the overall quantum system of which it is a part.

Eigenstate
A particular state within a quantum superposition.

Electron
Sub-atomic elementary particle belonging to the Lepton family of particles. Carry's a negative elementary charge to the value of 1.

Emergence
An emergent entity is one that displays properties which originate not within any of its parts directly, but which come about as a result of the interactions of those parts.

Entanglement - When quantum information is shared between different physical entities, meaning they are described by a single wave function, and can no longer be viewed as distinct entities.

Entanglement Entropy
A measure of the degree of entanglement in a many-body quantum state.

Entropic Gravity
AKA 'Emergent Gravity'. A background-independent theory of quantum gravity. Describes the emergence of Spacetime from the entropy of entanglement between sub-systems of the universal wave function.

Entropy
A measure of the disorder that exists in a system.

Eternalism
A philosophical viewpoint concerning the ontological nature of time, which holds that all times coexist on an equal footing - a view which follows as an inescapable result of the theory of Special Relativity.

Event Horizon
A boundary beyond which events can have no affect upon an observer; typified in astrophysics by the 'surface' of a black hole.

Flow of Time
The subjective experience of motion through time.

Free Will
The power of acting without the constraint of necessity or fate; the ability to act at one's own discretion.

Fungible
Not just identical, but also readily interchangeable.

General Relativity
Einstein's classical theory of gravitation.

Gravity
The 'force' of attraction that is caused by the warping of space and time due to the presence of mass.

History
See 'World-line'.

Inertial Frame of Reference
A frame of reference in which a body with zero net force acting upon it, does not accelerate. I.e. such a body is at rest or moving with constant velocity.

Information
A quantity relating the number of binary digits required to encode a message.

Information Theory
Theory dealing with the quantification, storage, and communication of information. Proposed by Claude Shannon in 1948.

Inseparability
See 'Entanglement'.

Lagrangian Mechanics
A alternate formulation of classical mechanics, in which the past, present, and future are all handled in an even-handed manner. Formulated by the Italian-French mathematician and astronomer Joseph-Louis Lagrange in 1788.

Light Cone
The path that a flash of light, emanating from a single event (localized to a single point in space and a single moment in time) and traveling in all directions, would take through Spacetime.

Light Year
A measure of distance - the distance that it takes light one year to travel in a vacuum (9.4607×10^{12} km).

Locality
The idea that no signals can propagate through space at speeds greater than the speed of light.

Loop Quantum Gravity
A background-independent theory of quantum gravity, based upon timeless finite loops from which it postulates Spacetime is constructed.

Many Worlds Interpretation
AKA the 'Theory of the Universal Wave Funtion'. AKA the 'Relative State Formulation'. An austere reading of quantum mechanics introduced by Hugh Everett, which asserts that the universal wave function has objective reality, and that its dynamics according to the Schrödinger equation should be interpreted literally - leading to an emergent web of parallel histories.

Matrix Mechanics
A formulation of quantum mechanics created by Werner Heisenberg, Max Born, and Pascual Jordan in 1925. Shown to e equivalent to the wave mechanics formulation of Erwin Schrödinger.

Moment
See 'Now Slice'.

Momentum
A vector quantity describing the physical property of an object, whose magnitude is the product of the objects' mass and velocity.

Multiverse
The ever-branching web of emergent, almost-autonomous, quasi-classical histories that results from the natural evolution of the quantum wave equation. Fist described by the physicist Hugh Everett in his 1957 paper 'The Relative State Formulation of Quantum Mechanics', which was also later published as 'The Theory of the Universal Wave Function' in 1973. Not to be confused with the multiverse that is associated with the theory of Cosmic Inflation.

Now Slice
A plain of Spacetime along which events appear to occur simultaneous with one another from the perspective of a given observer.

Path
See 'World-line'.

Photoelectric Effect
Physical effect in which electrically charged particles are released from a material when it absorbs electromagnetic radiation.

Photon
A quantum of light.

Plain of simultaneity
See 'Now Slice'.

Planck length
The smallest possibly discernible unit length of distance.

Planck time
The smallest possibly discernible unit length of time.

Plurality
The fact or state of being plural.

Position
Location relative to a particular system of co-ordinates.

Principle of Least Action
Physical principle from which the laws of motion can be derived. States that nature always minimises the Action quantity of a mechanical system.

Quantum
A discreet amount of something - a quantity.

Quantum Mechanics
Physical theory dealing with the behaviour of matter and radiation primarily at the atomic and subatomic scales.

Quantum Theory
See 'Quantum Mechanics'.

Qubit
A quantum bit - the quantum version of the classical bit used in computer science.

Realism
The idea that reality exists independently of what is measured by any observer - E.g. that a particle has a definitive value for a given property before anyone looks.

Singularity
A point of zero volume of space, consisting of infinite density and fearsome gravitation.

Spacetime
The 4-dimensional continuum of one time-like and three space-like dimensions.

Spacetime block
All of 3-dimensional space across all of time - The central concept of the 'Block Universe' view of reality.

Spacetime diagram
A 2-dimensional graphical representation of Spacetime. Of great use in gaining a qualitative understanding of time dilation and length contraction in the theory of Special Relativity.

Spacetime Interval
The mathematical 'distance' between two events in 4-dimensional Spacetime.

Special Relativity
Experimentally confirmed physical theory concerning the relationship between space and time.

Spin
Fundamental property of elementary particles, composite particles, and atomic nuclei, referring to an intrinsic form of angular momentum.

Standard Model of particle physics
The theory describing three of the four known fundamental forces (electromagnetic, strong, and weak. Gravity is excluded), as well as classifying all known elementary particles.

Superposition
The overall quantum state of a system, consisting of many individual eigenstates all at once. A system that is in a superposition is in many (potentially contradictory) states at the same time.

The Everywhen
Poetic description of the Spacetime block. The word 'everywhen' I've borrowed from an Australian aboriginal concept related to 'the dreaming', which embraces times past, present, and future.

Time Dilation
The slowing of the rate at which time passes for one clock relative to another. Occurs as a result of relative motion, and also as a result of exposure to a difference in gravitational potential.

Uncertainty Principle
Mathematical principal asserting a fundamental limit to the precision with which the values for certain pairs of physical properties of a particle can be predicted from initial conditions.

Universe
Spacetime, and all it contains.

Universal Wave Function
The quantum mechanical wave function of the universe.

Vector
A quantity possessing both magnitude and direction.

Wave Function
A mathematical description of the quantum state of an isolated quantum system.

Wave Function Collapse
Theoretical adjunct to the natural evolution of the wave function, dealing with the 'collapse' of a superposition from many eigenstates, to the single eigenstate that is observed upon measurement. First proposed by Niels Bohr in 1927, and one of the central tenets of the 'Copenhagen Interpretation' of Quantum Mechanics.

Wave Mechanics
A formulation of quantum mechanics created by Erwin Schrödinger in 1926. Shown to be equivalent to the matrix mechanics of Heisenberg, Pascual, and Born.

Wave-particle Duality
The quantum mechanical concept that every particle may be described as either a particle or a wave.

White Hole
The hypothetical inverse of a black hole; A region of Spacetime which cannot be entered from the outside, and from which all matter and radiation must be necessarily ejected.

WMAP
Wilkinson Microwave Anisotropy Probe.

World-line
The path traced by an object in 4-dimensional Spacetime.

The strangest of the strange,

How static rivers flow,

Through branches of a tree,

Which cannot ever grow,

So many many Nows,

So many many I's,

All present and correct,

In thunderstruck surprise...

Works Cited

[8] Bohr, Niels. As reported in *Discussions about Language*, 1933.

[5] Carroll, Lewis. "Chapter V: Advice from a Caterpillar". *Alice's Adventures in Wonderland*. 1865, p 41.

[18] Deutsch, David. *A Measurement Process in a Stationary Quantum System*. Oxford University Mathematical Institute, October 1990, p 1.

[11] ---. *The Fabric of Reality*. The Penguin Books Ltd, 1997, p 51.

[12] ---. *The Fabric of Reality*. The Penguin Books Ltd, 1997, p 217.

[15] ---. *The Fabric of Reality*. The Penguin Books Ltd, 1997, p 278.

[6] Eddington, Arthur S. *The Nature of the Physical World*. New York: Macmillan, 1928, p 91.

[2] Einstein, Albert, (quoted). Shankland, R. S. "Conversations with Albert Einstein". *American Journal of physics*, Vol. 31, January 1963, p 47-57.

[4] ---. *Time's arrow: Albert Einstein's letters to Michele Besso,* 1955.

[9] ---. From a letter to Schrödinger, 22 December 1950.

[16] Feynman, Richard. *The Character of Physical Law.*
Cambridge, Mass. : M.I.T. Press , 1965, p 162.

[3] Geroch, R. *General Relativity from A to B.* University of Chicago Press,
Chicago, 1978, pp. 20-21.

[7] Haldane, J. B. S. "Essay 34: Possible Worlds". *Possible Worlds and Other
Papers.* Harper & Brothers Publishers, New York, First edition in
1927, pp. 298-299.

[17] Ringbauer, Martin and Rafael Chaves. *Probing the Non-Classicality of
Temporal Correlations.* arXiv:1704.05469v2 [quant-ph], 14 Nov 2017, p 1.

[10] Schrödinger, Erwin. "Discussion of Probability Relations between
Separated Systems". *Proceedings of the Cambridge Philosophical Society,*
vol. 31, issue 04, 1935, p 555.

[13] Thorne, Kip S. *Black Holes - The Most Luminous Objects in the Universe, But
No Light!* California Institute of Technology, 2012, p 4.

[1] Wheeler, John. "Hermann Weyl and the Unity of Knowledge" *American
Scientist,* Vol. 74, July-August 1986, pp. 366-375. Reprinted in *At
Home in the Universe,* 1993, p 71.

[14] ---. *Geons, Black Holes, and Quantum Foam: A Life in Physics.*
W. W. Norton & Company, 2010, p 235.

Before thine eyes,

The past receding,

Behold the dawn,

The world has turned!

Into the sky,

See colours bleeding,

On bended knees,

We bow in awe.

Bibliography

Albert, David Z.
Quantum Mechanics and Experience.
Harvard University Press, 1992.

Ashtekar, Abhay and Tomasz Pawlowski, Parampreet Singh
Quantum Nature of the Big Bang:
Improved Dynamics.
Phys Rev D - Particles, Fields, Grav and Cos, Vol. 74, Issue 8, 2006.

Ashtekar, Abhay.
Loop Quantum Cosmology:
An Overview.
Gen. Rel. Grav. Vol. 41, 2009, pp. 707-741.

Aspect, Alain and Philippe Grangier, Gerard Roger.
Experimental Tests of Realistic Local Theories via Bell's Theorem.
Physical Review Letters, Vol. 47, No. 7, 17-Aug-1981, pp. 460-463.

Experimental Realization of Einstein-Podolsky-Rosen-Bohm
Gedankenexperiment: A New Violation of Bell's Inequalities.
Physical Review Letters, Vol. 49, No. 2, 12-Jul-1982, pp. 91-94.

Experimental Test of Bell's Inequalities Using Time-Varying Analyzers.
Physical Review Letters, Vol. 49, No. 25, 20-Dec-1982, pp.1804-1807.

Barbour, Julian.
The End of Time:
The Next Revolution in Our Understanding of The Universe.
Weidenfeld & Nicholson, 1999.

Bell, J. S.
On the Einstein Podolsky Rosen Paradox.
Physics, Vol. 1, No. 3, 04-Nov-1964, pp. 195-200.

On the Problem of Hidden Variables in Quantum Mechanics.
Reviews of Modern Physics, Vol 38, No. 3, Jul-1966, pp. 447-452.

Bojowald, Martin.
Absence of Singularity in Loop Quantum Cosmology.
Phys.Rev.Lett.86, 2001, pp. 5227-5230.

Brown, H. R. and D Wallace.
Solving the measurement problem:
De Broglie-Bohm loses out to Everett
Found Phys 35, Apr-2005, pp. 517–540.

Brukner, C. et al.
"Quantum Entanglement in Time"
arXiv: Quantum Physics (2004): n. pag.

Bryan, K.L.H and A.J.M. Medved.
The Problem with the Problem of Time.
arXiv:1811.09660[quant-ph]. 08-Nov-2018.

Cao, ChunJun and Sean M. Carroll.
Bulk Entanglement Gravity Without a Boundary:
Towards Finding Einstein's Equation in Hilbert Space.
Phys. Rev. D 97, 086003, 03-Apr-2018.

Carroll S.M
Something Deeply Hidden:
Quantum Worlds and the Emergence of Spacetime.
Oneworld Publications, 2019.

Carroll S.M., Sebens C.T. (2014)
Many Worlds, the Born Rule, and Self-Locating Uncertainty.
In: Struppa D., Tollaksen J. (eds) Quantum Theory: A Two-Time Success
Story. Springer, Milano.

Costa, F. and M Ringbauer, M E Goggin, A G White, A Fedrizzi.
A Unifying Framework for Spatial and Temporal Quantum
Correlations.
Phys. Rev. A **98**, 012328, 26-Jul-2018.

Deutsch, David.
Quantum Theory as a Universal Physical Theory.
International Journal of Theoretical Physics, Vol. 24, No. 1, 1985.

A Measurement Process in a Stationary Quantum System.
Oxford University Mathematical Institute, October 1990.

The Fabric of Reality.
Allen Lane The Penguin Press, 1997.

The Structure of the Multiverse.
arXiv:quant-ph/0104033, 06-Apr-2001.

The Beginning of Inifinity: Explanations that Transform The World.
Allen Lane, 2011.

Deutsch, David and Patrick Hayden.
Information Flow in Entangled Quantum Systems.
Proc. R. Soc. Lond. A 456, Jul-2000, pp. 1759-1774.

DeWitt, Bryce S.
Quantum Theory of Gravity. I. The Canonical Theory.
Physical Review, Vol. 160, No. 5, 25-Aug-1967, pp. 1114-1148.

Quantum Mechanics and Reality.
Physics Today, Vol. 23, 9, 30, 1970.

DeWitt, Bryce S. and N. Graham.
The Many-Worlds Interpretation of Quantum Mechanics. Princeton
University Press, 21-Nov-1973.

Dirac, P. A. M.
The *Quantum Theory of the Emission and Absorption of Radiation.*
Proceedings of the RSL, Series A, Vol. 114, 1927, p 243

The Lagrangian in Quantum Mechanics.
Physikalische Zeitschrift der Sowjetunion, Band 3, Heft 1, 1933, pp 64-72.

Einstein, Albert.
*Concerning an Heuristic Point of View Toward the Emission and
Transformation of Light.*
Annalen der Physik, 17th March 1905, pp.132-148.

On the Electrodynamics of Moving Bodies.
Annalen der Physik, 30-Jun-1905, pp. 891-921.

*On the Movement of Small Particles Suspended in Stationary Liquids
Required by the Molecular-Kinetic Theory of Heat.*
Annalen der Physik, 17, 1905, pp. 549-560.

Does the Inertia of a Body Depend upon its Energy Content?
Annalen der Physik, 18:639, 27-09-1905.

On the General Theory of Relativity.
Königlich Preußische Akademieder Wissenschaften
(Berlin).Sitzungsberichte 11-Nov-1915, pp. 778-786.

Einstein, Albert and Boris Podolsky, Nathan Rosen.
*Can Quantum Mechanical Description of Physical Reality Be
Considered Complete?*
Physical Review, Vol. 47, 25-Mar-1935, pp. 777-780.

Everett, Hugh.
"Relative State" Formulation of Quantum Mechanics.
Thesis, Princeton University, 1957.

Eyo Eyo Ita, III, Chopin Soo, Hoi-Lai Yu.
Intrinsic time quantum geometrodynamics.
Progress of Theoretical and Experimental Physics, Vol. 2015, 8, Aug-2015.

Feynman, R. P.
Space-Time Approach to Non-Relativistic Quantum Mechanics.
Reviews of Modern Physics, Vol. 20, No. 2, Apr-1948, pp. 367-387.

*Mathematical Formulation of the Quantum Theory of Electromagnetic
Interaction.*
Phys. Rev. Vol. 80, 440, 01-Nov-1950.

Giulini, Domenico and Erich Joos, Claus Kiefer, Joachim Kupsch, lon-
Olimpiu Stamatescu, H. Dieter Zeh.
*Decoherence and the Appearance of a Classical World in Quantum
Theory.*
Springer, Berlin, Heidelberg, 2003.

Gribbin, John.
*In Search of Schrödinger's Cat:
Quantum Physics and Reality.*
Corgi Books, 1984.

Heisenberg, Werner.
Quantum Theoretical Re-interpretation of Kinematic and Mechanical Relations.
Zeitschrift fur Physik, 33, 1925, pp. 879-893.

Hensen, B., Bernien, H., Dréau, A. *et al.*
Loophole-free Bell inequality violation using electron spins separated by 1.3 Kilometers.
Nature 526, pp. 682–686 (2015) .

Jacobson, Ted.
Thermodynamics of Spacetime:
The Einstein Equation of State.
Phys.Rev.Lett.75, 06-Jun-1995, pp. 1260-1263.

Entanglement Equilibrium and the Einstein Equation.
Phys. Rev. Lett. 116, 201101, 20-May-2016.

Kaku, Michio.
Parallel Worlds
The Science of Alternative Worlds and Our Future in the Cosmos.
Allen Lane; Doubleday, 2006.

Maldacena, Juan.
The Large N Limit of Superconformal Field Theories and Supergravity.
Adv.Theor.Math.Phys.2, 22-Jan-1998, pp 231-252.

Maldacena, Juan.
The Large N Limit of Superconformal Field Theories and Supergravity.
Adv.Theor.Math.Phys.2, 22-Jan-1998, pp 231-252.

Marletto, C amd V. Vedral.
Evolution Without Evolution, and Without Ambiguities.
Phys. Rev. D 95, 043510, 13-Feb-2017.

Mermin, N. David.
It's about Time:
Understanding Einstein's Relativity.
Princeton University Press, 2005.

Minkowski, Hermann.
The Relativity Principle. Lecture given at the meeting of the Göttingen Mathematical Society. 5-Nov-1907.

The Fundamental Equations for Electromagnetic Processes in Moving Bodies. Lecture given at the meeting of the Göttingen Scientific Society. 21-Dec-1907.

Space and Time. Lecture given at the 80th Meeting of the Natural Scientists in Cologne. 21-Sept-1908.

Moreva, E and G Brida, M Gramegna, V Giovannetti, L Maccone, M Genovese
Time from Quantum Entanglement:
An Experimental Illustration
Phys. Rev. A **89**, 052122, 20 May 2014.

Moreva, Ekaterina . and Marco Gramegna, Giorgio Brida, Lorenzo Maccone, Marco Genovese.
Quantum Time: Experimental Multi-Time Correlations.
Phys. Rev. D 96, 102005, 24-Oct-2017.

Newton, Isaac.
The Principia:
Mathematical Principles of Natural Philosophy.
05-Jul-1687.

Olsen, S. Jay and Timothy C. Ralph.
Entanglement Between the Future and the Past in the Quantum Vacuum
Phys. Rev. Lett. 106, 110404,17 March 2011.

Olsen, S. Jay and Timothy C. Ralph.
Extraction of Timelike Entanglement from the Quantum Vacuum
Phys. Rev. A **85**, 012306, 4 January 2012

Padmanabhan, T.
Thermodynamical Aspects of Gravity:
New Insights.
Rep. Prog. Phys., Vol. 73, 2010.

Page, Don N. and William K. Wootters.
Evolution Without Evolution:
Dynamics described by Stationary Observables.
Physical Review D (Particles and Fields), Vol. 27, Issue 12, 15-Jun-1983,
pp. 2885-2892.

Penrose, Roger.
Cycles of Time:
An Extraordinary New View of The Universe.
Vintage, 2011.

Ringbauer, M. and R. Chaves.
Probing the Non-Classicality of Temporal Correlations.
Quantum 1, Vol. 35, 14-Nov-2017.

Ringbauer, M., Costa, F., Goggin, M.E. *et al.*
Multi-time quantum correlations with no spatial analog.
npj Quantum Inf 4, 37, 2018.

Rovelli, Carlo.
The Strange Equation of Quantum Gravity.
Classical and Quantum Gravity, Vol. 32, Number 12, 1-Jun-2015.

Reality is Not What it Seems.
Allen Lane, 2016.

The Order of Time.
Allen Lane, 2018.

Rovelli, C. and L. Smolin.
Loop Space Representation of Quantum General Relativity.
Nuclear Physics B, Volume 331, Issue 1, 05-Feb-1990, pp 80-152.

Spin *Networks and QuantumGravity.*
Phys.Rev. D52 04-May-1995.

Saunders, S, and J. Barrett, A. Kent & D. Wallace (eds.).
Many Worlds?: Everett, Quantum Theory, & Reality.
Oxford University Press UK, 2010.

Schrödinger, Erwin.
Quantisation as a Problem of Proper Values (Part I).
Annalen der Physik (4), vol 79, 1926.

Quantisation as a Problem of Proper Values (Part II).
Annalen der Physik (4), vol 79, 1926.

On the Relation Between the Quantum Mechanics of Heisenberg, Born, and Jordan, and that of Schrödinger.
Annalen der Physik (4), vol 79, 1926.

Quantisation as a Problem of Proper Values (Part III).
Annalen der Physik (4), vol 80, 1926.

Quantisation as a Problem of Proper Values (Part IV).
Annalen der Physik (4), vol 81, 1926.

Four Lectures on Wave Mechanics.
Delivered at the Royal Institution, London, on 5th, 7th, 12th, and 14th March 1928, London and Glasgow: Blackie and Son, Ltd., 1928.

Schwinger, Julian (Editor).
Selected Papers on Quantum Electrodynamics.
Dover Publications, Inc, 1958.

Sebens, Charles T. and Carroll, Sean M. (2018)
Self-Locating Uncertainty and the Origin of Probability in Everettian Quantum Mechanics.
British Journal for the Philosophy of Science, 69 (1). pp. 25-74.

Shannon, Claude.
A Mathematical Theory of Communication.
The Bell System Technical Journal, Vol. 27, pp. 379-423, 623-656, Jul, Oct 1948.

Silberstein. M. and W. M. Stuckey, Timothy McDevitt.
Beyond the Dynamical Universe:
Unifying Block Universe Physics and Time as Experienced.
Oxford University Press, 2018.

Van Raamsdonk, Mark.
Building up Spacetime with Quantum Entanglement.
Gen Relativ Gravit, Vol.42, 2010, pp. 2323–2329.

Verlinde, Erik.
On the Origin of Gravity and the Laws of Newton
J. High Energ. Phys. 2011, 29 (2011).

Wallace, David.
Everett and Structure.
Studies in the History and Philosophy of Modern Physics 34, 2003, pp. 87-105 .

The Emergent Multiverse:
Quantum Theory According to The Everett Interpretation
Oxford University Press, 2012.

Wallace, D and C. Timpson.
Quantum Mechanics on Spacetime I:
Spacetime State Realism.
The British Journal for the Philosophy of Science, Vol. 61, 4, 2009.

Wheeler, J. A.
Superspace and the nature of quantum geometrodynamics.
Topics in non-linear physics, 1968., pp. 615-724.

Wootters, W.K.
"Time" replaced by quantum correlations.
Int J Theor Phys 23, 1984, pp. 701–711.

Zeh, H. Dieter.
On the Interpretation of Measurement in Quantum Theory.
Foundations of Physics, Vol. 1, 1970, pp. 69-76.

Zhao, Z. and R Pisarczyk, J Thompson, M Gu, V Vedral, J F Fitzsimons.
Geometry of Quantum Correlations in Space-time.
Phys. Rev. A 98, 052312, 12-Nov-2018.

Zurek, Wojciech H.
Decoherence and the Transition from Quantum to Classical.
Physics Today, Vol. 44, Issue 10, 1991, p 36.

Decoherence, Einselection, and the Quantum Origins of the Classical
Rev. Mod. Phys. 75, 715, 22-May-2003.

Zurek, Wojciech Hubert and Juan Pablo Paz.
Decoherence, Chaos, and the Second Law.
Theoretical Astrophysics, Los Alamos Nat Lab, 03-Feb-1994.

So welcome then to the unending,

Born an infant to this world,

Gifted with a life eternal,

Untold realms are thine to roam...

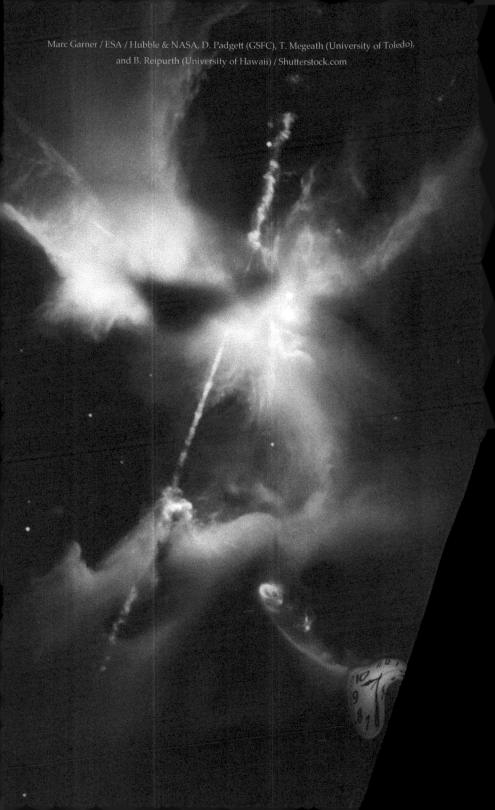